To Mum & Dad,
Happy Anniversay!
Love
Erin x

Mater & Pater
Happy Thingy 33
Love
Carol xxxx

Mustn't Grumble

POSY SIMMONDS
Mustn't Grumble

JONATHAN CAPE

TWENTY VAUXHALL BRIDGE ROAD

LONDON

to Richard

First published in this collection 1993
3 5 7 9 10 8 6 4 2

© Posy Simmonds 1993

Posy Simmonds has asserted her right
under the Copyright, Designs and Patents Act, 1988,
to be identified as the author of this work

The drawings in this book have been taken from
cartoon strips that appeared in the *Guardian* and the *Spectator*

First published in the United Kingdom in this
collection in 1993 by Jonathan Cape
Random House, 20 Vauxhall Bridge Road, London SW1V 2SA

Random House Australia (Pty) Limited
20 Alfred Street, Milsons Point, Sydney,
New South Wales 2061, Australia

Random House New Zealand Limited
18 Poland Road, Glenfield,
Auckland 10, New Zealand

Random House South Africa (Pty) Limited
PO Box 337, Bergvlei, South Africa

Random House UK Limited Reg. No. 954009

A CIP catalogue record for this book
is available from the British Library

ISBN 0-224-03844-3

Printed in Great Britain by
Clays Ltd, St Ives plc

A Calendar *from* 1988

January

Miles Upmaster (42), L.M.X.[1] Broker at Johnson, Duff, Morant (*Reinsurance Brokers Ltd.*) is Man of the Month!

Miles effs and blinds his way into the New Year, as he does through Life...as well he might! His Christmas was a scant four days of *total knackerdom*, at home in Parsons Green, with wife, **Vanessa** (36) and daughters, Jojo and Davina.

Absolute ******[2] nightmare it was!

Vanessa had jaundice, Jojo had nits and Khyber was on heat:

O Gard!

And it's the usual *Oh-Christ* situation back at J.D.M..... *everything* should have been quoted two weeks ago...and placed, but renewals have come in late....

...The assumed quote I was banking on the Atlantic Re[3] is N.T.U.[4]...*******s[5] want 4 reinstatements at five on line... ·.

And **Su**, his secretary is about as much use as a f*rt in a colander...***never*** feeding his meter, spending hours in the bog, spraying her **glue-do**[6]

Bye, Miles ..see you

Take care

....and, living, as she does, in Southend, she's always belly-aching about the Fenchurch Line, ...late in and **b*gg*ring** off early. (Leaving Miles to do all the faxes.)

There's little cheer ahead for Miles....the odd binge at Balls Bros, a monster p*ss-up **or two** at Langans....

...But **skiing**'s off this Spring... ..got to help the *International* side with Japanese renewals... ..s*d it!

Costive and splenetic, Miles lights his fifth King Edward Half Corona and contemplates a few *Low Flyers*[7] at the Grapes[8] with Jebbetts' scratch boy[9]...

GLOSSARY
1 London Market Excess
2 Expletive deleted
3 Reinsurance
4 Not Taken Up
5 Expletive deleted
6 An elaborate coiffure
7 Famous Grouse Whiskies
8 A hostelry in Lime St
9 Underwriting assistant at the Jebbett syndicate at Lloyds.

February

Design Consultant, Chloë Banister (37) is <u>woman of the month</u>:

Log'eau
DESIGN CONSULTANTS

Deep in Soho, with partners, Mervyn, (strong on conceptual thinking) and Rodney, (solid financial backing), Chloë is a power house of target-based creativity...and makes a bomb.

Commercially AWARE and self-motivated, *interior*-related projects are Chloë's *forte*..... currently, the re-vamp of millionaire, Sir Clive Rudbern's fashion chain is on Log'eau's books....

> BASICALLY, WE'RE THINKING
> *DISTRESSED* WOOD & BRICKWORK
> THRU-OUT...THE **CLOTHES**'LL BE
> DISPLAYED ON **V.D.U.**s...AND
> <u>NO</u> PLANTS...

▶ It's all a long way from Weymouth Grammar and Saint Martin's School of Art (where Chloë wore a black beret the entire three years).. ...a long way from her days as just a graphic designer, doing photographers' *letter-heads* and the odd company report, from a back room in Clerkenwell.

Success these days means a house in Dulwich Village with husband, Hugo, (a TV commercials director), infant, Jack, (who's down for *Westminster*), and an Icelandic nanny. It's a **Life Style** not without sacrifice: Chloë often misses Jack's bedtime, never has time to read *The Independent* – delivered daily— and had to get rid of the cat, when she decided to wear **black full time**.

▲ And culture only gets a tiny look-in: Her heroes are Marcel Duchamp ● Matisse ● Brian Eno ● Eileen Gray. She plays "difficult," music at work (intellectual rock, Mahler's 2nd). Sometimes, (when no-one's around), with one of her Bakelite phones in one hand and a tissue for the lipstick trace on her upper canine in the other, she will pause for a blub over Mahler's Fifth.

MARCH

A Bedrock of the British Tourist Industry is woman of the month

Jackie Green (29), seasonal taxi driver / bed & breakfast landlady / daily help / baby sitter / bar assistant at the *'Play Waves'* Marina Complex / *Wife* and mother of two.

Jackie Green loathes her letter box...a treacherous slit, that admits official letters and final demands into her home. It also lets in unsolicited DREAMS and these are worse...DREAMS of *Interest-free credit loans...* of luxurious double glazing...of fabulous Golden Lifestyle Prize Draws....

Bonrose

DEAR MRS GREEN

Here's a wonderful piece of news!! The **GREEN FAMILY** has six - yes, **SIX!!** - chances of winning one of our valuable Dream prizes, **Plus** a brand new super Bonrose catalogue...**plus** a fabulous extra £5000 Quick Reply Dream Bonus, if you send off the YES envelope **NOW!**

Numerous are the YES envelopes that Jackie has despatched...**NIL** are the dreamy Vauxhall Nova Star prizes won... but **MANY** are the fabulous fashion-filled catalogues received, aburst with super home ideas, that tempt, tantalise & sour the temper...

Ian's been laid off the quarry six months with his back...there's **NO** work for me till the visitors start coming in June...and even then, B & B's no good anymore...it's all self-catering - caravans & holiday flats, now...

...the car's on its last legs... and as for the PRICES!! I mean, I was born here, but I can't afford to live here!

Life outside Jackie's letterbox is even worse for her: "Crab Pots" and the dozen other 2nd homes she minds for their owners, are chock-full of super home ideas: *microwaves, patio loungers, dish washers, dog duvets, combination freezers, blenders, co-ordinating covers and curtains, modular barbecue systems...*

And they're only used less than 3 months a year. MAKES YOU PUKE!

Well, we can't bloody afford ANY of it! We're in DEBT! ...Gas...rent...H.P..you name it!

Poor Jackie, continually harassed to buy, borrow and squander.....Asked if she liked living in an idyllic, picture book village, she'd reach for the **NO** envelope...

A P R L

Visitors, Desmond!

Desmond Duff, (82), a retired engineer, very lame and rather deaf, a resident of Deddinham Court Rest Home, is man of the month.

Desmond's son & daughter-in-law are ushered into his room by Mr & Mrs Hirst, proprietors of Deddinham Court.

"Hallo, Strangers!" bawls Desmond, instantly prompting in his visitors the urge to chuck their Paschal tribute at his old, white head.

I MEAN, **REALLY!**...COME AS OFTEN AS WE CAN!.. JUST DRIVEN **70 MILES!!**

"Welcome to the Hell Hole!" continues Desmond, causing Mrs Hirst's mouth to purse like a hen's bottom. John and Penny know what this implies: a *mauvais quart d'heure* later in her office.....

...WE DO HAVE A *VURRY* LARGE WAITING LIST...IF HE GOES ON LIKE THIS, I REALLY **MUST** ASK HIM TO LEAVE...HE'S BECOME *VURRY DIFFICULT!*

Desmond *HAS* got difficult... a life-long, true-blue party member, he's turned...well, very **BOLSHIE**, sitting there in his room, writing **STINKERS** to John Moore.

John & Penny compose themselves for a litany of grievance:
● The Hirsts are **LEECHES**, the fees they charge, an absolute **RAMP!**

● The Government penalises **THRIFT**: Desmond has been mug enough to save for his old age, thus disqualifying himself from any State help.
● His aged TV has conked and he can't afford a new one.
● Deddinham Court has a brisk turn-over of over worked and under paid staff.
● They leave him sitting for hours on the bally commode.
● Ga-ga residents keep barging in-to his room at night.
● Last Rations are at 5p.m...his belly rumbles all night.
● Instant mashed potato is served seven days a week.
● He never sees hide nor hair of an **EGG**.
● Mr Hirst has **NO RIGHT** to wear a Rifle Brigade tie.
● Nothing has been done about the pong on the landing.
● The local hospital is still almost the same shambles of nissen huts that it was in the war, and they can't do his knee for another six months.
● His Christmas cactus has root rot.
● Mrs Lomax & Miss Bate told Mrs Hirst that they no longer seek his company, because he pulls his nose hair during Scrabble.

●

Driving back to Clapham, John and Penny, voice their own mantra of despair....

Oh dear. oh dear. oh dear !! WHAT does one do?! Oh dear!... Oh Lord! Oh dear. oh......

A GENTLEMAN RIDING WITH A HOUND
dated 1988

Oil on canvas 39 × 49 in (99 × 124·4 cm)
Private collection

The sitter is identified as MR ROBIN CHUTNEY-DARKE, *a dealer in* C18th *&* C19th *English painting, with premises,* (BREAM & DARKE), *in St James's.*

He is posed against his property near SWINDON, where he lives with his wife and family.

ROBIN CHUTNEY-DARKE *was educated at* ETON *and* AGNEWS, *(he began there as a porter), and set up his own business with* CHARLES BREAM *c.*1972. He *is the subject of several other paintings, notably:*

● GENTLEMAN SITTING AT THE WINDOW TABLE AT CECCONI's.
● GENTLEMAN FLYING SWISSAIR AS PASSENGER WITH PAINTING.
● GENTLEMAN RACING AT CHISWICK. (CHUTNEY-DARKE *races a two year old Mercedes on the flat between* SWINDON, *his town house in* S.W.3 & *his office.)*

His cri de coeur, when buying, is: "Chr✳st, this sale is cr✳p!" ... and, when selling: "In two years time, this'll look a STEAL!".....and in the saleroom, the surfaces of the many, heavily restored paintings 'cause him endless grief..."LINOLEUM would be an improvement....."

June

Katie Gillyman, 7, (and to some extent, her mother), are *persons of the month....*

Dear Kelly......
Please come to my party on June !
at 62 Lynwood Road
from 4.30 till 6.30
From Katie

Katie's friends look foward to her birthday... for Katie's parties are *really* **BRILLYERN!**

There's a *Care Bears* theme-table, a *Wuzzles* cake, **REAL,** grown-up *canapés*...there are party Poppers.. **HELIUM** balloons ...a **CLOWN**, hired for 5.30 p.m.... and the *Going-Home Loot Bags* each contain a swag of *glitter-pen*, transfers, milk chocolate kittens, *SnowMan* pad... **AND** a *Magic Message Pony!*

... *Imagine*... **TWO** weeks' house-keeping blown on **TWO** hours of fun!

But Katie's Mummy believes it makes sense: *perhaps* it's some **reparation** for being out at work all week...and certainly, it's a way of saying thank you to those other mummies, who fetch and deliver and entertain her daughter throughout the year.

Mummee! They're HERE-YAH!

A Brilliant Party means every-body observing the **PARTY CODE**......It means each guest, on arrival, paying with an entrance parcel,...which will be ripped apart in the Opening Frenzy and for which the donor expects small thanks.

O, I got one of *these!*

It means allowing the birthday girl her licence to shriek, cheat and generally misbehave.

It means a sweet wrapped up in **EACH** layer of *Pass the Parcel*... it means immodest dancing to *Madonna* records...it means prizes for winners **AND** losers.. ..it means food chucked on the flower bed...it means the **CLOWN** being paid £56, by cheque, sharp at 6.00 p.m...it means the par-ents collecting their kids on time and not hanging about for gin... ...It means a *whole* day off work and makes a crater in the bank balance...it means Katie feeling **SICK** by seven o'clock, ...but not *half* so sick as the departing mummies......

GOD! I MEAN, THE EXTRAVAGANCE! ..ALL RIGHT FOR HER - 2 INCOMES

JUST SHOWING OFF!

D'YOU KNOW HOW MUCH THIS STUFF COSTS? *WICKED!*

JULY

This July, think kindly upon those huddled masses that slump in airport lounges...and, in particular, have pity for the **couple** at LUQA airport....
Tony McVitie and his bride, Lorraine.....

FIVE hours they've been waiting in the heat..."owing to the lateness of incoming flights from Gatwick".

FIVE HOURS HANGING ABOUT LIKE A F*RT IN A SLEEPING BAG....

But the *real* blight on Lorraine and Tony's honeymoon, whose major features should have been legs up, leglessness and legover, concerns...well...Lorraine's **legs**.
Lorraine's legs deserve the very maximum of public exposure...and, indeed, when they first swayed off the plane ten days ago, the eyes of Malta never left them ....running up and down their glabrous length, from the **six**-inch steel tips in the south, to the tiny, linen pelmet in the north. **HOW** Tony basked in their reflected glory!.... a glory, alas, short lived....

By **DAY TWO** of the honeymoon, it was **HANDS OFF LORRIE'S LEGS**, burnt to blistering in the Maltese sun. And, on **EVENING FIVE**, as the couple ate their swordfish at Marsaskala, the mosquitoes struck beneath the table....

YOU NEVER SAW SUCH BITES! 21 OF 'EM! I TOLD HER NOT TO SCRATCH!

Now, imagine Lorrie's legs: ruddy, blotchy, itchy, stinging, swollen... ...all she could do was groan "Oh God!"...until last night, when, after scrutiny in the shower...

MAD FOOL, I THOUGHT: I CAN'T GO HOME WITH HAIRY LEGS...SO I STARTED SHAVING 'EM...Ooh, THE AGONY!

Lorraine's legs are **STILL** the cynosure of all eyes – she packed *only* minis, nothing *covering*. Tony mans a proprietorial barrier of Duty Free bags around the stricken limbs...for there's a Libyan lady, who stares and stares...and an English geyser, in a smelly blazer...

AND YOU CAN ALL STOP STARING, TOO!

August

There's a drab, sodden tinge to the meadow....
There's a drab, sodden tinge to the meadow.....
The corn is as flat as a day-old cow pat....
And the rain is a-raining on Farmer Hughes' hat....

O what a bloody pigs' breakfast!
O what a terrible mess!
I've got a horrible feeling.....

The Horrible Feeling of August's Man of the Month, Mike Hughes, is that he's right in the silage: 100 acres of corn are up the spout. Now, he must homeward plod his weary way, and at his computer, get his arithmetic RIGHT for the year ahead.

ARITHMETICAL PROBLEM:

If a farmer has 250 acres, a herd of 90 dairy cows, a P registration Range Rover, a wife doing evening classes in book keeping and a son who wants to design table lamps, when he leaves art college... if the corn is wet and sprouting and 50% of the cows, dry and calving...if milk output is down and interest rates, feed prices and cases of Bovine Spongiform Encephalopathy are up, what should the farmer be planning?

Should he cut his herd by 20%, but try to maintain his milk yield by asking Fred if he can lay his hands on some Bovine Somatrotropin?
Should he rent his Set Aside land to caravans..or to clay pigeon shooting..or to trail bikes? Should he start an enterprise with deer..or goats or quail..or trout ..or carp ....or snails..or...or..?

A COUNTRY SAW:
If St Bartholomew's Day be clear,
A prosperous autumn comes that year.......

September

Woman of the Month is Prissie Rugeley, mother of four and wife of an infantry officer, stationed in West Germany.

Prissie's quite calm, considering the usual hoo-hah. Today, she's got to get her husband off on exercise and herself and the four monsters to the U.K.

Tiggy's name tapes haven't arrived, she's lost her leotard, Nicko, his clarinet..and James's green maggot* absolutely PONKS!

However, in a minute, Prissie will check under the car for bombs and take poor old Doglet to the Frewings...(Angela's jolly noble about having him)...then she'll nip to the N.A.A.F.I....the chaps at the gate will check her I.D. and the boot and under the car.....

...and she'll return all the blasted videos to the N.A.A.F.I. shop...and get back home in time to retrieve the green maggot from the tumble dryer.....and to kiss James goodbye....

Then Suki arrives: switch off and lock up and everyone into her car.... and a thrash up the autobahn...and then a delayed flight at Gutersloh...and poor Bubba frightfully sick as the plane circles & circles above Luton, where her sister, Celia, waits & waits to meet them (in VAIN, when the plane is diverted to Gatwick),.....Then, it's the

* Army sleeping bag

train to Victoria and God knows what hour they arrive at Celia's ...complete limp rag department!

"Oh sh*ttykins!" thinks Prissie, imagining the frantic days ahead...the mammoth shoe-buying...the cross country dashes depositing the three big'uns in their separate schools in Hatfield, Dorset..Godalming.

Then, it's back to Germany, to the empty quarter, to wait with Bubba & Doglet for James's return from the Brigade F.T.X. in a 443 area to the south of Detmold, and the Adventure Training exercise in Bavaria.

She's not the captain of her fate, posted hither and yon on the strength of her husband's C.R...but she jolly well makes the best of it. In spite of bombs and Red Alerts, the prospect of a ghastly posting, no part-time jobs and not much loot to be made flogging beads at the Bielefeld Flower Club, she stays capable and calm – that's Prissie...with the pink pigs rushing in circles round her sweater.

October

CROUCH, James Dalston; Writer since 1950; *b* 12 March 1929; *S.* of Eric Crouch and Ann (née Bates); **m** 1st 1957 Barbra Hope (marr.diss); one *s.* one *d.* 2nd Sophie Watt 1975; one *s.* Educ: Chelmsford Grammar Sch., Wadham Coll. Oxford; National Service (Army) R.E.M.E.
Publications: Last Bus from Braintree 1958; filmed 1960, adapted I.Tv. 1982; Out of Flatley, 1960; Cold Norton, 1963; Bonds of Strife (selected essays) 1966; Women, Flats and Fields (stories) 1967; Wakering Blow, 1972; The Scouring Breath 1978; filmed as Wings over Walberswick, 1980; The Harlow Years, 1986; Up Bardfield, 1987; Round Trip to Nowhere, 1988.
Recreation: Philately; *Address:* % Perry & Davis Ltd, 16 Sill St, London W.1.
...is October's Man of the Month.

Near the taxi queue at Euston, they said farewell. Their last **brief encounter** was over and there was little left to say. Yet, still she fretted over him: had he enough cigarettes...what time would he arrive back in **Braintree**...would he be hungry...would he really NOT accept money for his ticket..? And still she tried to reassure him...their day together had not been a failure...that all was well.

They stood, a sad mésalliance of **Spring** and **Autumn**: she, the publicity girl from Walmer & Wilcox, so young, so efficient... ..he, the author of a new novel, tired and spent. Her job of accompanying him during the publicising of his book (a few signings & interviews in the provinces), was now over. Soon, a taxi would take her to a younger man, a man of promise, who she would escort to the party held in honour of his second novel, (his first – shortlisted for the Booker Prize), and who, in subsequent days, she would tenderly shepherd to all those venues, where his talent would be fêted: Broadcasting House, Camden Lock, Lime Grove, Hatchards, the Groucho Club.

HE CAN'T STRING A SENTENCE TOGETHER ...BUT HE'S A **CLEVER LITTLE CREEP!**

Crouch remembered his own days of glory, his name blazoned over the literary pages, the pyramids of his books in Foyles' window, the queues of people agog for his signature...the murmured compliments...the triumphant flourish of his pen on countless title pages.....

Best wishes J.D.Crouch.

But now, public taste has changed: Social Realism is the genre of yesterday and the publication of his new book merited no more than a few cursory and, in some cases, slighting mentions in the press...and, today, in Manchester, only 6 punters wanted their copies signed....

NO! YOU SIGNED EIGHT! AND IF IT HADN'T RAINED, LOADS OF PEOPLE WOULD'VE COME!

And Crouch rued the changes at his publishers, once congenial, with committed editors & lunches, but now, as part of an international conglomerate, it disgorged huge advances for pulp and packaged his own work in lurid jackets.

Thus Crouch boarded his cab, feeling the onset of winter..the taxi heater was on and the butter, in its dish in Braintree, would be hard.
"Bye Bye", she said, "Take care!"

November

November: the cold deepens, the nights lengthen. Wherever the atmosphere grows frosty, the smiles get wintry, the waiters stiff and the diners chilly...then, there you'll find the Man of the Month,......
..... SIMON SANDERCOCK

Simon Sandercock, 33, single, Company Director, rugger player.

Whenever Simon gets up flying speed, EVERYONE (a) *is in absolute* FITS (b) FALLS ABOUT (c) WETS *themselves... because Simon is:* (i) PRICELESS! (ii) *completely* MAD (iii) *a* HOOT!... *and* (iv)....

> AN *ABSOLUTE SCREAM!!!* HE'S SAY FUNNY!!

Simon is JUST *brilliant! At the drop of a fork, he can perform:*
- *The whole of* ESKIMO NELL
- *The* ENGINEER'S SONG
- 250 KNOCK-KNOCK *jokes*
- *An extensive range of bathroom noises, on the soft part of his forearm, including the* CUSHION CREEPER *and the* ONION BUMBLE.

PBWEEB!

Simon also does really, really brilliant impersonations of Basil Fawlty and Prince Charles and Inspector Clouseau..... ...he can do SCREECHINGLY *naughty things with matches and match boxes and £10 notes........ ... and, if it's an Italian restaurant, Simon always gets everyone to set fire to their* AMARETTI *biscuit papers, to see whose paper rises the highest:*

..and it's so hysterical...whole table gets completely covered in ASH!
But Simon's absolutely BEST *thing is to ask the waiter if he's ever seen a* CLOTH-EARED ELEPHANT! *And it's just killingly funny, because Simon then takes out the insides of both trouser pockets and then starts to undo his zip...and the waiter goes absolutely* CHERRY RED!! *...And then, sometimes, Simon actually takes his trousers off...and he and everyone get booted out... .... and it's just* SO...SO...
AMUSING.

DECEMBER

Bringing a seasonal glow to tiny hearts...December's Man of the Month is... FATHER CHRISTMAS....

FATHER CHRISTMAS *doesn't live in the North Pole with his reindeer. And Father Christmas' real name is* **GERALD.** *He lives in Maida Vale, with a telephone that seldom rings.*

If one looks hard through a copy of **SPOTLIGHT,** *one discovers that Father Christmas is a man of many parts:*

● *For 3 years he was Assistant Stage Manager at Kidderminster Rep.*
● *He played several inconsiderable rôles in* "**Z CARS**" & "**COMPACT**".
● *His big break was playing a Pharisee in* "**SON OF MAN**" *in the mid 60's. This was followed by a season with the* **R.S.C.,** *where he was a memorable* Rosencrantz.
● *Later, he played* **Macduff** *in the Scottish Play at Frinton Rep.*
● *His television work includes one commercial – he was a most convincing* **TEA BAG** *...and he was one of a number who just missed getting the* **MR KIPLING** *voiceover.*

Of late, Gerald has been living off the odd computer payment: (£1·23) from the sale of **EPISODE 19** *of* "**The Rise of Eagles,**" *to Kuala Lumpur...and is used to putting on a good act in the dole queue in Chadwick Street.*

SEE YOU'RE NOT WORKING, LOVEY

ACTUALLY, JUST HAD AN AVAILABILITY CHECK FROM GRAMPIAN

.. ALSO HAD A WEST END OFFER....

Indeed, he has a **WEST END** *offer. His agent,* **LEWIS HARRIS,** *said it wasn't quite panto at The Palladium...but it was definitely undivided attention and a captive audience.*

So, here he is on the **4th** *floor of* **DORKSON'S,** *his grotto full of tiny, mewling people.*

"Ho, ho, ho! And what would **YOU** *like for Christmas?" he asks in his pleasant baritone, a* **FISHERMAN'S FRIEND** *masking every trace of his lunch-hour noggins. It matters not that the* **STAFF TOILETS,** *where he applies beard & brows & rosy cheeks, are a far cry from a dressing-room at Chichester. because.....*

Christmas comes but once a year, And when it comes, it brings **£110 p.w. EQUITY MINIMUM.**

Six *Bounden Duties*

Six *Bounden Duties*.... No.1: Conservation

A statement *(with subtitle facility for the hard-of-hearing)*, by *Aubrey Shyte*, present owner of 'Rakesham Park' [Listed, Grade II].

I was both **shocked** and **saddened** * to read the recent correspondence in the local paper...

* Needed my brown trousers

...whereby **certain** parties laid **SERIOUS allegations & criticisms** at my door.... concerning the changes I am bound to make to the **Deer Park** and to the estate...

TWO generations of **Shytes** have lived here at Rakesham①, and I and my family ② are **very** sensible of the **ENORMOUS PRIVILEGE**③ and accompanying **DUTY**④, of continuing to ⑤ **preserve** this lovely house ⑤

① Father bought it cheap in the 30's ④ Nightmare
② My accountants ⑤ Bloody White Elephant
③ Financial suicide

...which is why we find these accusations of **PROFITEERING** and **ENVIRONMENTAL RAPE** frightfully hurtful...don't we, darling?

Oh, simply GHASTLY!

...and so, to be **utterly FRANK**...whatever **tittle-tattle** you may have heard...the **BOTTOM LINE** on this one is...**absolutely NO way** will I ever sell the **Deer Park** for development...**NO way** will it ever go under brick...*

* **NO** way will those *Local Planning* sods and the *Department of the Environment* **LET** me.

On the **contrary**, you should all appreciate the very **positive** attempts at **preservation & conservation** that I have made:

I suffered **terribly** from **WIND** last October, as I think we all did....but have lost **no time** in replacing damaged timber...*

* 60 acres quick-grow conifer enterprise

...I've been greatly concerned with the welfare of the **deer**... ...have topped up their numbers...*

* two hundred fold

...**Deer** are such **SHY** creatures...it's my one ambition that these **super** animals, which have **roamed** here for **so** long, should continue to thrive in **complete seclusion**....

...and that is why, with **GREAT** reluctance, I have sought permission to **close** the **public footpath** through the **Park**...and to erect high **deer fences** around its perimeter....

We humans have much to learn from **creatures** of the **wild***. . . .

* Hopefully, how to develop *deer embryo transplantations* & a whole *genetic breeding programme*, with *laproscopic insemination* etc

..and I know that the honour of caring for them is a **marvellously enriching*** experience...

GGGGrrFF!

* **Farmed venison** production is going great guns: **2,500 U.K.** carcases last year, due to increased continental demand. Current retail prices are:
Saddle of venison .... £5·00 per 1b
Haunch .... £5·20 per 1b
Stewing ...... £2·75 per 1b

Please, Please... Allow me...**help me** to **preserve** their **peace***....

* So, **FOXtrot OFF!** all you veggie activists, walkers and other loonies!

No bones broken, eh?

Thanks awfully

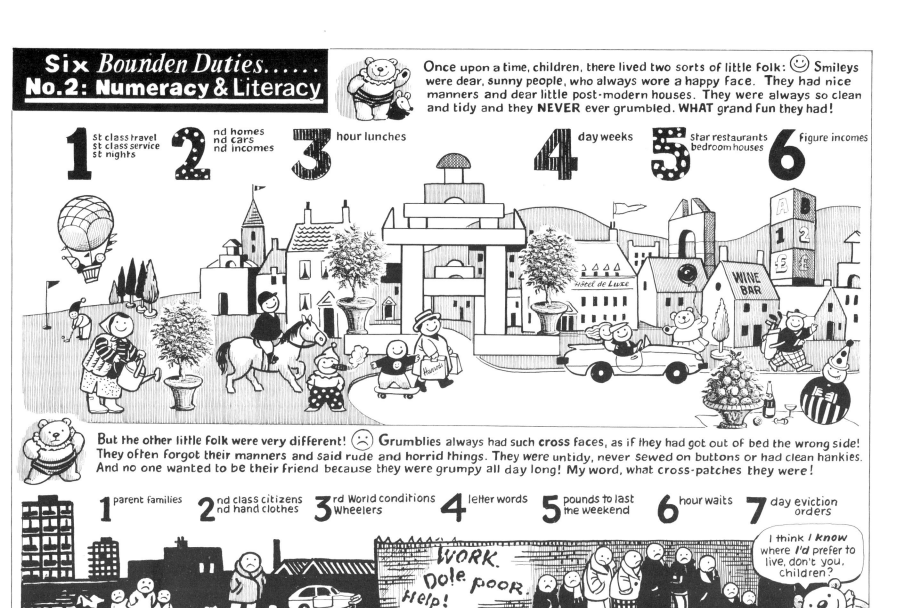

Six *Bounden Duties*.....
No.3: A Sense of Humour

COMIC FUN

JOHN & JAN

GOSH, JOHN! WOMEN'S EARNINGS ARE **STILL** ONLY 66% OF MEN'S

YES, DEAR

AND **HALF** OF ALL FAMILIES ON OR BELOW THE POVERTY LINE ARE HEADED BY **LONE MOTHERS**...

YES, DEAR.

..76% OF ALL WOMEN GET **LESS**...

JOHN! YOU'RE NOT PAYING ATTENTION!

OF COURSE I AM, JAN!.. YOU KNOW HOW I LOVE WOMEN'S **FIGURES!**

ZEEBOD 2050 A.D.

EARTH FOOLS!

THE OVERALL ANNUAL **RADIATION DOSE** ON YOUR PLANET IS TOO **LOW!** GET IT **HIGHER!!**

OUR GOVERNMENTS'RE **TRYING!** THEY'RE DOING THEIR **BEST!**

BARFIE

DO YOU KNOW THE HEALTH GAP BETWEEN RICH AND POOR HAS WIDENED..?

AND DEATH RATES FOR **TOP** CLASS MEN HAVE DECLINED BY **37%,** AS OPPOSED TO **7%** IN THE LOWER TWO CLASSES?

NO, BARFIE, BUT IF YOU HUM THE TUNE, I'LL PICK IT UP AS I GO ALONG!

MATEY

EE, THERE'S A LOT OF **MALE CHAUVINISM** AT WORK!

EH? COME AGAIN? ...WHAT'S MALE CHAUVINISM, WHEN IT'S AT 'OME?

YOU, yer LAZY SOD, – THAT'S WHAT!

"Gosh, I'm really worried about the hole in the ozone layer...."

"No, you can't go on reading the News....you're beginning to look middle-aged!"

"Did you know the R.S.P.C.A. had to put down 59,832 dogs in 1986?"

"Ow! It's raining ACID!"

LOST PROPERTY

"We've lost our jobs!"

Six *Bounden Duties*... No.4: Keeping the Lines of Communication open

© P. Simmonds 1988

Six *Bounden Duties*.....
No. 5: Not to Change one's Spots

 ..but we're still the same people we were..say, ten... twelve years ago...

....True, the **CAR's** changed..... SIGH...I really *blubbed* when it had to go...it was *such* an old friend...

 But we **SAVED** all the **stickers**....the **WHALE**..NUCLEAR POWER, NO THANKS...the **baby seals**..

No! WE haven't changed...

Well, you know.. few **wrinkles**... ..bit less hair...**these** monsters have grown..

The kids **won't** let us put them on the new car....but we've got them safe....

 See, we needed something a **BIT** bigger for the **wind surfer**...well, **AND** for going to the country....

And **this** is so **QUIET** on the motorway...

Same old street..**same** old house.. well, **except** for a few improvements..

Well, the poor old **sag bags DID** get a bit clapped out..and we **were** all **really** on top of one another....

..So we added this bit on the back...

..just a bit of **ADULT** space..but it's handy when people come round...

The neighbourhood's still the same..well, *bit* more pricey....the local school's ...well, actually, the local school's **NOT** the same... ..Lucky Bill and Ned went there when they did....

And **WORK**..well, still the same..still doing the cards, wrapping paper...posters...

One or two more shops

POSTER/PAPER

Same good old posters, still selling well...

..specially the '68 ones, this year...

And.. **politics**...well, you know, ...it's not **US** that's changed... ...it's the Labour Party....

Funny, really, isn't it?.....

..cos **we** haven't changed a bit..

© *Posy Simmonds* 1988

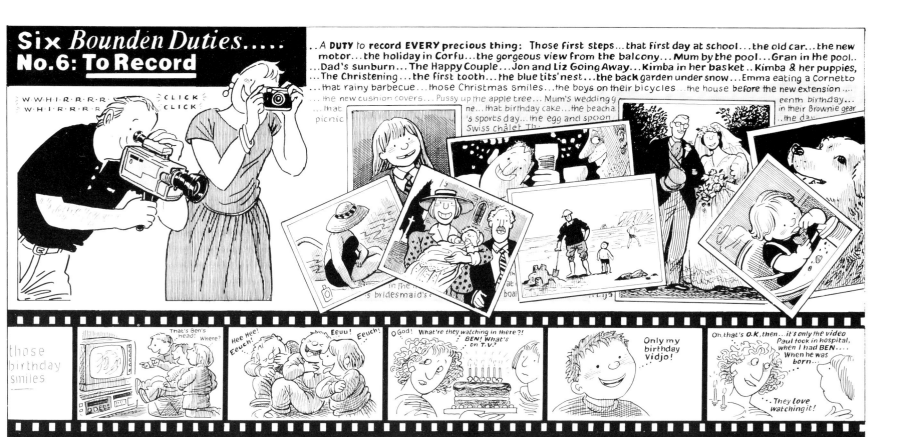

THE CHERRY ORCHARD (etc)

Aaah, Sonia... HOW happy we all once were... here in our little, weekend dacha...

SIGH

...with the birch grove behind and the land-owner's cherry orchard before....

© Posy Simmonds 1987

...SIGH...all the festivals of the year we spent here.... ...Easter...Whitsun.... ...Christmastide....

So many weekends...for so many years, Sonia....

Aah, yes, Ivan...

...Aaah, I think of your clogs, Sonia... ...of you in your peasant skirt...and me in my Dylan cap...my Zapata moustache...my cheese-cloth shirt...

Do SHUT UP, Rosa!

Owh! When are we going back to LONDON!?

HOW simply we lived in those days! ...Living off the land...nettle soup, dandelion salads....in the autumn, we grubbed under the beech trees...

They're not MUCK, darling...they're called cèpes... they're absolutely SCRUMMY sautéd in butter & garlic!

When are we going back to London?

Eeuch!

...We made our own amusements.......

But WHY couldn't we bring the PORTABLE here?

Owh!

For the last time, I'm NOT having TELLY down here! ..You watch QUITE enough at home!....now, come & finish your corn dollies...

... And after each perfect day, we would lie, lulled by the scent of cherry blossom....and the sounds of moths and mice and our little children coughing...

cough Hoch hoch!

But NOW the cherry orchard is SOLD!!

Aai! Ai! Sonia!

SOLD!

The cherry orchard is SOLD!!!

The landlord sold it to developers.....

BLOODY PEASANT!

And you know WHAT!! NOW there's a SODDING great GARDEN CENTRE opposite us!

Garden Centre

Shrub

...with planning permission for toilet facilities, play area and VIDEO shop !!!

... And every weekend, the mercantile classes arrive in swarms...and cram their cars full of dwarf conifers, compost and hybrid gnomes....

Aai! Ai! Sonia!

Garden Centre

If only we could go back to MOSCOW ROAD...SELL the house, FINISH our life here, and go back to LONDON!

Ai! Ai!

Brillyern idea, Mum!

Hard **Times** (1992)

Hard Times

Late one evening, after a **SOW** of a day in the City, **Miles Upmaster**, (a reinsurance broker at Jebbson, Duff, Morant), returns to find his home glowing with warmth and light....

*Godsake, Vanessa!..the heating's **on!***

*Turn it **OFF!**..and these lights!*

*Just burning **MONEY!***

*But it was like a **MORGUE** here.. **FREEZING!**..and the **Crouches** came... so I had to..*

*You had people **in?***

I thought we agreed..no more people to dinner!

*Was only **polenta** and plonk in the kitchen...*

*Vanessa, I don't want people here...I don't want them **knowing** our troubles.*

*Well, I **can't go OUT!** ..if we still had a **nanny**, I wouldn't be going **bonkers**, walled up here with with the children...!*

*We can't **afford** a **nanny**...or her **poll tax**... We can't afford **ANYTHING!***

*Listen, Vanessa... **read my lips**...**WE ARE IN DEEP TROUBLE**..*

*Deep **DOO-DOO** ...understand?*

*The **market's** contracted ..I've had **NO** profit commission for **90** or **91**..*

*We're **stuffed** with **RUN-OFF** losses — **pollution** and **asbestosis**...*

*..we've got **CAT. 91 ABC & D's** spiralling up our **backsides***

*When the **LMX** department integrates with the inter- national side, I'll be **lucky** if I end up placing **Direct Spanish Fire FAC/OBLIGS**..*

*..**Rumour** has it I'll **be out on my arse**, Vanessa..!*

*Then it's **bed of nails** for **US**...the **mortgage** screwed..and the **school** fees....no **PENSION**... ...no **BUPA**..no car...*

*No one'll feel sorry for us...they'll all **love** it!*

Ouhh... Hardship!

Hard!

Hard!

*I'm on the **RACK!***

Uuh!

*I'm hitting **ROCK BOTTOM!***

*Life's so **HARD!***

An Explanation by J.D. CROUCH Author

At Home J.D. CROUCH: Literary Lion's a pussy-cat at home!

THIS is an early copy of a forthcoming issue of **CHARISMA** magazine, in which, **I** and my family are featured...

I wish to make it plain to readers of my novels, that this *'interview'* was undergone as part of my **contractual** obligations with my publishers, **Walmer & Wilcox** (*now part of* **DYNAGLOBE INTERNATIONAL**). In the present economic crisis, I am bound to cooperate with the publicity department in their **every** effort to promote my new novel*

* *Hard Core*/£14·99 published April 9th

Readers of my books will know that, in the past, I have been acclaimed for the **stark realism** of my work; my attempts to expose **pretension & hypocrisy** have not gone **unnoticed**:

"*Crouch catches with unfailing honesty the brutality of our times.*" — *The GUARDIAN*

"*A classic of its genre, Last Bus to Braintree, is deeply felt... relentlessly honest.*" T.L.S

"*A bleak indictment of human pretensions* The lady

In other words, my concern is for **total HONESTY**...which is why I find these **BLATANT distortions** of the **TRUE** facts of my domestic life **deeply offensive!**

The Crouches are early birds and breakfast's a time of shared laughs over cuppas!

These pictures are full of **embarrassing LIES!**.....
...**lies** contrived by **Terry**, the photographer and **Lyn** the stylist...

THOSE are not our **crocks**! ...ours are heavily stained and chipped...as for the **tulips** – our house is a stranger to **CUT** flowers!

...And **I** never take breakfast: I work in my room and speak to **NO ONE**, except my **DOG**, until noon.....
But Terry refused to take me alone at my desk

Look! I wanna shot with loadsa **warmth**!

Get your **wife** and **kids**..OK?

I said my young children were at school and my wife upstairs, working... I said he could take me with **SHEBA**. (*My poor dog, currently, has Sarcoptic Mange, which I treat with skin baths*).

Gross!

Eventually, of course, my wife was **dragged** from her work and my son, by my first wife, from his bed. **Both** were **surly**....**Sophie** and my marriage is going through a **BAD** patch...and **Daniel** has much to reproach me for, when I left his mother....

Godsake! SMILE!!

Sophie only managed to smile after she asked me, *point-blank*, if I was sleeping with **Dido Phipps**

No, she turned me down.

Ooh!

Daniel began smiling, when he was asked to **HUG** me, because he knows that I find demonstrations of affection **embarrassing**:

I, in all honesty, could find **NOTHING** to smile at.......
Then Terry exhorted me to think of the **MONEY** and the **boost** this degrading feature will do to my flagging sales...

Great! Love it!

Hold it!

© Posy Simmonds 1992

Mid-Life LIBIDO
In Forward & Reverse

It is lunchtime, chez novelist **J.D. CROUCH**:

That **BOY**'s asking for a good *larruping* with a **strop**!

What, now?

I will **NOT** have *this* house used as a **knocking shop!** I will **not** have him bringing his **pick-ups** back here!

Tsk! **REALLY!**

Look.. I go in the upstairs **khazi** – there's this **WENCH** in there... using **your** tooth brush!.. clearly just emerged from **Daniel's** bedroom!

Wasn't his friend, **Lizzy**..

.. was a most **depraved** and **UNAPPEALING** little piece...all in tight, shiny **black**... looked like a yard of **black pudding**

I don't think that generation's ever heard of the **LOVE AFFAIR** ..it's all *instant self-gratification* for them... **Micro-wave sex**..they want it **HOT! NOW!**

..No self-restraint ..no moral values ..only what they learn off **T.V** ...

They'll never know what it's like to **worship** a **WOMAN**!.. those long voyages of sensual discovery...

Those heights!

..**depths**

Those little deaths!

Enough!

First: DON'T call women "**pieces**"...

Second: Her name's *Amanda*

...She's an articled clerk

Third: She and Dan went clubbing last night, ...it was **safer** for her to come here, than to go home on her own...

Fourth.. as you're so interested..they're **NOT** sleeping together

WHAT!

How d'you know?

Dan told me... they're just **friends** ..she had his bed... he slept on the floor

...**Look**, he's very serious about being **celibate** at the moment.

DAMN FOOL! Attractive girl like that! **I** wouldn't have let **that one** get away in **MY** young day! **HO No!** I'd've **soon** sorted **her** out..**sharpish**!

Got **no PASSION**, these youngsters!..lot of little **cold-blooded puritans!**

She'd need a real man......**her** upstairs...**I saw**!...moved like an **EEL**, when she shut the door with her behind....

That fabric

..over her **rump**...

..**bloom** on it ...like a ripe **plum**...

Where **was** I? What did I come down for?

Daniel..using the place like a knocking shop

Yes!

Why isn't he?

..what's the **matter** with him?....

© Posy Simmonds 1992

Mens Sana

There's only one bathroom at my Dad's house...it's a **REAL** pain...**JUST as you've** got back from the **GYM**... and want to get ready to go out, **HE** chooses to have one of what he calls his **CREATIVE BATHS**.....

You'll have to wait, old boy

GOD! Dad!

Listen, Daniel, I am a **WRITER**... I know to **YOU**, a bathroom's just a place to exercise your **mindless narcissism**...

..But, to **ME**, it's a place for scouring the **mind**, as well as the **body**...the **khazi** is the...

FORCING HOUSE of **IDEAS! I know!** You said it **nine squillion times!**

Not only **THAT!** ..it's a place for the most rigorous scrutiny of one's **belief-system!**

...Something **YOUR** intellectually slothful and politically complacent generation...with its **worship** of **MATERIAL comfort** and pectoral muscles...can **NEVER** understand!

At your age, **my God**, we had **IDEALS**....

And, if you're really unlucky, you get, **YET** again, the full history of these massive wrestling matches he's had with his conscience, in all these crappy bathrooms

Like the freezing one, off Marchmont Street, in his bedsit days in the 50's...when he was a raving **leftie**...

...There was a geyser, **BRONCO**, a shilling in the meter...and him and Gunter Grass, **THE NEW STATESMAN**, Wesker, Thom Gunn and **THE GOLDEN BOUGH**..having wobblies about **SUEZ** and Hungary...

Then there was a slightly warmer bathroom in Chelmsford in the 60's, when he was writing "COLD NORTON"...He was in there with Ferlinghetti, Corso, Nathalie Sarraute and a candle-wick bog-seat cover, feeling gutted about Czechoslovakia....

In the **70's**, it was central heating, close carpets, pink **ANDREX** and a **PAMPAS** suite, in Camden. Dad calls the 70's **his AGE OF DISILLUSION**...it's when he split with my mum, made a packet when "**Last Bus From Braintree**," was filmed ...and when he started to read **The Daily Telegraph** as well as **The Guardian**....

The **80's**, he moved here, to Cusham Hill. The bathroom's the only bit he did up, ...that's where he sweated over his royalty statements and tax demands...

Anyway, he's got a **BLOODY NERVE** accusing **me** of complacency.. ...Worshipping material comfort

All he's doing in there is wrestling with a Michael Broadbent book on good **claret years**

I can point the finger, too...

J'accuse, Dad!

J'accuse!

JACUZZI!

© Posy Simmonds 1992

Club Ability

SOPHIE CROUCH is being treated to a drink in the Ladies Annexe of The PARNASSIAN CLUB. Recently, the PARNASSIAN voted against a motion to admit women as members...

You see, Sophie, it's **NOT** because we're **ANTI-WOMEN**..

'**Course** we're bloody **NOT**! We've **nothing** against women – on the contrary, we're always delighted to receive ladies here... **YOU** know that...

Oh, **I DO**, I do...

It's just a question of **LONG TRADITION**...very, very **HARD** to break....

Oh, yes, I do see

I **DO**

I quite understand... **MEN** need a **refuge**...from all sorts of things you don't want to think about at the end of a long day... ...which women members might remind you of...like having to bully the kids to do their homework....

Quite

And you always make it **SUCH** a lovely treat for women, when we come here, I can see how **GRACELESS** it could become... a woman could order herself a gin at the bar...and just **IGNORE YOU**...

Well, yes

Some women **ARE** bloody rude these days...

And, somehow, a lone woman sitting here drinking, at this hour, doesn't look right...

You think she should really be at home putting the children to bed....

Exactly

And they don't really know how to drink, do they..? ..they know nothing about **WINE**..or else they know **FAR** too much!

Sophie!

Oh yes! Bloody little smart-arses, some of 'em

And, as for the **SEX** complications, **IMAGINE** the humiliation of putting up for membership and being black-balled by your **EX-WIFE**!

SOPHIE!

yes..or by some little....

And, **IMAGINE**!..all those **dreary** husbands women'd bring here... ..and all the long hairs on the upholstery... lipstick on glasses ..all those **pheromones**!

Yes..trouble with women, is they're either **silly** or **earnest**... Silly ones're **BAD** enough..Earnest ones are the bloody **END**!

I tell you what would be my idea of **ABSOLUTE HELL**!.... and that's a gaggle of **media-hags**...or finding a lot of **huge-arsed** old bags monopolising the billiard room...

Simon, I think I have to ask Sophie to leave the club..I'm not inviting her here again...

She's not being entirely **SINCERE**

Crouch! Dear boy!..there I was thinking she was **one** of us!

Haves and Have·nots

OK, everyone...now, I want each of you to imagine you're a *little* **BULB**, in the dark earth

TINKLE TINKLE

...all waiting for this **cold**, **horrible** winter to pass.....so, start **curled up**.. **WAIT** for the **SUN** to start warming you...

..then, start **pushing** your leaves up..**up** through the soil...**reach up**..**reach** for the sky...

TINKLEY TINKLEY TINKLE

... and **all** of you are going to grow into *beautiful, tall*, proud **daffodils**!

TINKLEY TINKLE TINKLE!!

All right?

Right.. tight little BALLS, everyone..it's **cold**... ...now, feel the change in the air...**COME ON, Kim!** - **stop** looking at Ned... **tuck** those feet in, **Ned**!

TINKLE

Ooh..a bit **QUICK**, Ned! Try again... Come on the rest of you..**up** you come ...

Yeh!

Start feeling your **leaves** opening ..**show** your petals off...very good, Ned...

Come on, Gavin!

Heads UP! Stop looking at the Floor, Debbi!

Come on..you're all looking sad and wilty, except for Ned...**EVERYBODY** should be **tall** and proud...

That's not a **proud** head, Dominic..look at Ned..look what a proud daffodil he is!

Tsk! He's **not** being a daffodil! ..he's just showing off his **new** trainers!

Yeh!

New **Nike Airs**!

She's got Reeboks!

Not fair! Ned's got big feet..**mine** aren't big enough for **Air Nikes** yet...

They don't make small sizes

When my feet's big, I want Nike **180's**

Mum says they're too ex**pensive**, cos they're £69·99...SO I'll get Converse All Stars instead...

My mum can't afford ANYTHING

Lessee the soles... Are they Air Jordans or **Junior Max**?

Yours're **crap**! They got velcro fasteners!

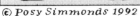

© Posy Simmonds 1992

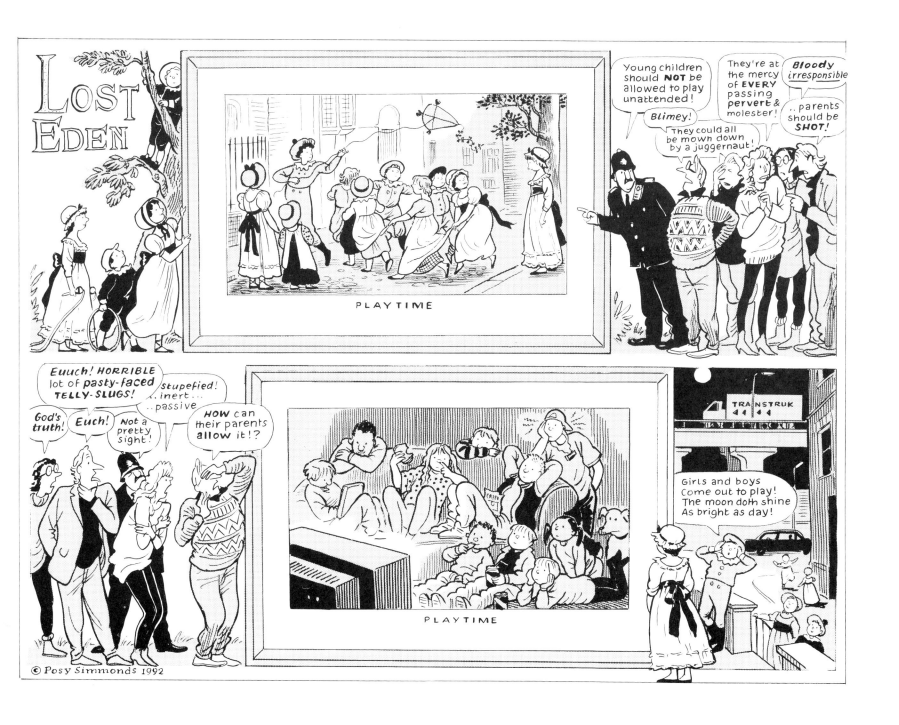

Noises Off

It's a regrettable fact that many of us never lose any sleep over the plight of the homeless..

ZZZ.. COUGH! COUGH!

...but there are SOME who don't lie easily in their beds at night.....

Oh God!

You see, he's down there again...in our porch...*coughing* and *coughing!*

It goes right through you... makes you feel QUITE ghastly ...poor man...

And you think there *must be* SOMETHING you can do...

WE HAVE tried..

...the second night we heard him, we offered him some money to pay for a bed in a hostel...

He said hostels were *N.B.G.* 'cos things get *nicked*...but he thanked us *very, very* much..and went off...he was *terribly* grateful...

And we felt, you know, this rather nice warm feeling....

...until we realised...

...all we'd done was to give him a fiver to go and cough on *someone else's doorstep!*..made us feel MORE awful!

You see, there's nothing you can do that doesn't smack of the most *odious* SELF-INTEREST!

Last night his cough was TERRIBLE!

And he was a bit *cross* when I woke him with some *Benylin*...

And I *said* we *really* sympathised and that the only answer was for people, you know, like *US* to put pressure on the Goverment to provide more jobs and cheap housing and things....

..Although I'm not *quite* sure how one does *that*

..And I said... meanwhile, was there ANYTHING we could do for him?

And he said there WAS..

Well..we can't really afford it..but we WILL do what he asked..and DOUBLE-GLAZE our bedroom...

You see, then we won't keep on disturbing him..

...and we'll sort of feel we're doing our bit....

© Posy Simmonds 1992

The Vileness of PENURY

At a select address in **Cusham Hill**, a door-bell rings....

...*Vanessa Upmaster's* **ex**- cleaner has come to collect some money.

Oh God! Sheena!

Come in! Come in!

I came Monday, but you were out...

Damnation!

I forgot!

I'm **SO SORRY**, Sheena! Can you **forgive** me!? ...I'm **SO SORRY**! **HOW AWFUL** of me..!

Just we're having such a **MEGA-BLOODY** time... ...**Miles** losing his job...

Where's my bag?

We **can't** sell the house... ...**Surveyor** says it's not worth what we paid for it... We're **mortgaged** up to the **hilt**...

We'll have to live in the **basement** ..and **rent** the rest.....

Kids've got to leave their school

..My job doesn't **BEGIN** to pay for child-minding

Anyway, here's your envelope...I'm **sorry** we can't afford to have you any more...

Oh, cheers

Well, we're **both victims** of the **recession**, now.. **both** in the same **boat**....

HARDLY, Vanessa! **I** wouldn't mind a **comfy** one, like this!

And you're **not** the only one of my clients to lay me off!

Oh **I KNOW**..I know it's **far worse** for **YOU**.... Believe me, I've learned a thing or two, lately... ..I **understand** now, how **AWFUL** it is for people living **hand to mouth**!

I just had **NO IDEA**, before..

But..at **least you** get some **sympathy**...

No one feels sorry for us **AT ALL**... They just think we **deserve** our **come-uppance**...

They'll just **love** it when the **bailiffs** come for the **antiques**...

SIGH!

Look, I'm **SORRY**, Vanessa..

You're sorry for us, Sheena? Well, **THANK you**....

NO..I'm **NOT!**..I'm sorry it had to end up with **POST-DATED CHEQUES!**

Common Market

NO shallots... **NO** rocket.. **NO** potatoes, except Edwards ..that's *typical* bloody England for you!

...talk about *Third World* country!... I *despair!*...I mean, in *French* markets, you get about six varieties....

Well, you can get **ANYTHING** in France...

..market we go to in *Libourne*..everything's *beautifully* displayed

They take a pride...

Not like **here**... Look at it..nothing but **boring** old root veg...piled up any old how!

Yes, Ladies?

No.. no point in asking you, if you've got any **rocket** ...

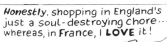

HOPELESS, this country! But what d'you expect?... **NO ONE's** really interested in **EATING**... and everything's so **crude**..there's no *finesse*...

SO depressing!

I mean, this bakery....

The **CAKES! NO** French *pâtisserie* could **BEAR** to display this lot...

CLODS of coconut..**LUMPS** of industrial "chocolate" cake....

..look as though they've been made by a **WELDER!**

Honestly, shopping in England's just a soul-destroying chore... whereas, in France, I **LOVE** it!

Market days there're **SOCIAL EVENTS** ..full of *joie de vivre*.... I have **tremendous** chats with the stall-holders...they're **so** friendly!...

Greet me like an old friend!

Here – no reason at all– they **SCOWL** at you....

© *Posy Simmonds 1993*

INSECURITY

*It's the hour of the **NIGHT·NOISE**....*

*...a time of psychical disorientation... when the **TINKLING** of **GLASS** might mean.....*

*When you peek through the curtains, the street's **ALWAYS** empty...just sodium glare and menacing shadow...*

*There are **LOUD** night noises.....
...terrific **THUDS**...*

*...**LOUD** human voices – the jovial farewells of late party-leavers, which curdle the blood*

*There're **SOFT** night noises...
...**LOWERED** human voices, which sound like **EVIL** conspiracies....*

*There are **BARELY AUDIBLE** night sounds, which are, somehow, the **WORST**...faint scratchings...**TINY CREPITATIONS**.....*

*You see, you can't tell these days, if you're threatened by **MICE** or **MANIACS**....it could be the sound of the **DETERMINED PROFESSIONAL**.... The One Who Can Always Get In.....*

*...And the hissing sound of an **OXYACETYLENE WELDING KIT**....*

*...is not **UNLIKE** the sound...*

...of the bloke who's having a pee in your doorway....

© Posy Simmonds 1993

Beneath the IVORY TOWER

The life of the writer is a hard one: LONG periods of enforced solitude are spent SCRATCHING away...

GRATZ! GRATZ!

...probing.....

...researching....

...extracting gravel.

Contact with the outside world is routine and limited.....

60   REGAL VEG.

..but provides an essential daily breath of air in Reality...

Honest! That's what I heard!

NO! Well I blame HIM! He's a cold fish!

TSK! It's those KIDS you feel for, don't you? Fancy having to read that about your parents!

See her at Ascot? Looked GUTTED, didn't she?

Oh, she DID!

mato's

Pea's

Hallo, there...think she's going to crack up, do you?...eh?

Who?

Di!

What?

Gor! where you bin?

Don't you read the papers?

No.. I don't read THOSE ...my wife won't have them..you know, with children around..

Not good for their English..

Pound of onions, please

And I don't care for this vicarious pleasure in people's misery

Oh, you mean chadenfreude?

Yeah

Tough, innit?

Anyway, I don't wish to read lurid speculation...

Pound of peas, too

By the way, peas don't have an apostrophe in the plural

Frankly, from the little I know, it's just an exercise to bloat a lot of hacks' wallets

Yeah.. stinks of the midden, doesn't it?

Quite!

And so, back to the grindstone....

Damn! Had this bit yesterday, with the spuds...

ROYAL CHARADE

Let's see what's round the onions..

SADDI WEPS

© Posy Simmonds 1992

Object Lesson

Ah.. there you are..

Phone messages... *Ian* wants you to pick him up at **9.00**... Dave rang.. so did *Toby*....

..s'ppose that means you want the car, again?

⸨ SNIFF ⸩

They're bastards!

What ever's the **MATTER?**

I'm fat

ugly

They're bastards

Oh fergoodnessake! There're **BOYS** ringing up every night *clamouring* for you to go here, there ....'s like *BEES* round the honey pot...

You should be so **LUCKY!**

I'm fat! ugly.... spotty!

You're **not** fat! You're **FINE!**

..you're just refusing to conform to an outmoded stereotype... you're just... *alternatively sized...*

Pfuhh! **Alternatively sized!**

You mean I'm *proportionally challenged?*

Yeah?

I'm *visibly sebum assertive...* **Acne-friendly?**

I've got *positive·variform featuring?*

Do wussafavour, Mum! - I'm **PLUG-UGLY!**

Uch! Can't listen to any more of this **HORRIBLE** *whingeing!*

I mean, if you can't see yourself as others see you...

You're incredibly *popular*...always in demand...

..always off with a **car**-load of **boys**

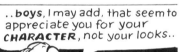

..*boys*, I may add, that seem to appreciate you for your **CHARACTER**, not your looks..

..something that didn't happen in *my day*...

..and something you can thank **MY** generation for... all those battles we fought for women to be treated as <u>people</u>...

...I just find it completely wonderful...a **TRIUMPH**... that your boyfriends don't treat you as a *sex object*...

No, they **DON'T,** Mum...

They wouldn't look at me twice....it's only 'cos I'm the *only* one in our lot who's passed their *driving test*.....

They treat me like a *taxi*....

Treat you like a **TAXI**!?

My god!..The little....

Think I'd rather be a sex object

© *Posy Simmonds* 1992

Dating a SINGLE PARENT

Zat **NEW**, Mum?

Ah! That's Ian! Rring!

GrFF!

Hang on... must just say a quick byebye to the kids

Bye bye, Polly! Be back soon! Hi, Polly!

Where's **Frankie**? ...she'll read you a nice story... **where's** she **GONE**?

NO!

Dohwanter!

Bwerrrr

Frankie!

Francesca!

Where **ARE** you?

Francesca! ..are you in there?

Bwwerr!

Come and look after Polly... we want to go now!

I'm doing my **REVISION**!

Godsake! look after her.. **PLEASE**! You **said** you would

But I got my **MATHS**!

Werhrr

Don't be so **BLOODY UNREASONABLE**!

Mum! I got an **EXAM**!

You don't **CARE** about my exams!

You just care about **HIM**!

How **could** you say that!?!.. I've got a right to a social life..!

Sorry, Mum.

There... there ...it's all right

AHEM!

Oh..Ian! Gosh..we ought to...

Bye, Mum! Bye, darlings

© Posy Simmonds 1992

Fireworks

Oooh! Aaah!

Oh God!.. Grandpa and Emma arguing again!

YOUR generation needs a ROCKET up its backside!

Ooh! Ooh!

BANG!

Aaah! STOP whining about having no *future!*

STOP wallowing in this APATHY... this DEFEATISM!

Things were just as terrible for my generation ...WE didn't whinge... .....WE grew up in a depression...

Well, so do I! I remember mass unemployment... hunger marches...

So? Woss different?

KABOOM!

Now, now, now, Daddy!

YOUR age, I was fighting Hitler!

we KNOW you went through hard times ...but you have to sympathise with Emma....

Oh, shuddup, Mum ...nothing t'do with YOU!

Yes!

What d'you KNOW about it?

YOUR generation!...Ye Gods!...You had it jammy! ..cream AND jam!....

Sixties boom time..Education frothing with money.. JOBS galore...cheap flats to rent

I didn't go to university

..scrimped so YOU could!

Huge grant you had

..which you didn't have to pay back

Dropped in and out of jobs, as you pleased....

Went bumming off to India and god knows where in smelly vans!

WE never had SEX lives like YOU... all on the PILL...

and AIDS-free!!

Ooh, you lot had it JAMMY!

CUSHY! CUSHY! CUSHY!

WE had it H·A·A·RD!

We have it H·A·A·RD!

Aaah!

Ooh!

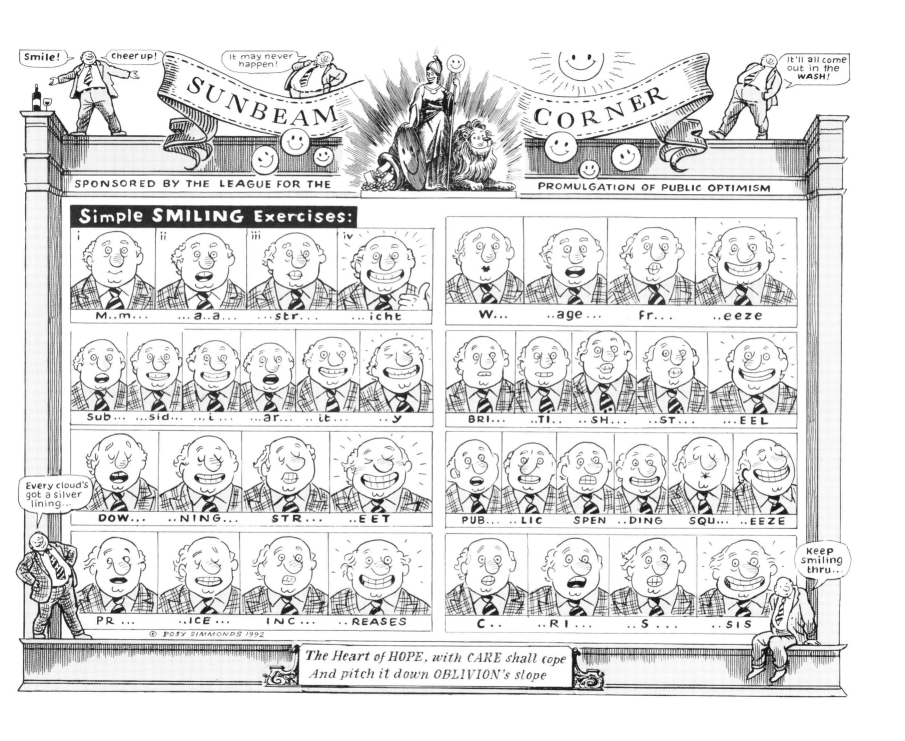

A **Calendar** *from* **1989**

Janvier

Voilà Mme Rutherford.... *la Femme du Mois:*
Elle s'appelle **Hazel**. She teaches **French** at a boys' comprehensive. She has pastoral responsibility for the 4th year. She has two small sons at primary school. Her husband works in a garden centre.

Mrs Rutherford *raises a* FLASH CARD *and asks for the second time:*

ALORS, GAVIN!
QUEL TEMPS
FAIT-IL?

GAVIN *does not respond. Gavin is busy. All the boys are busy, priming their watches to go off at five minute intervals. The watches make pretty tunes – c'est tellement drôle! But, at last, Gavin does reply:*

IL FAIT PLEUT, MISS...
OUI, OUI.. WEE-WEE!
IL FAIT PLEUT

...and the whole class falls about: wee-wee – c'est rigolo!

Yes, it is raining.. raining *des cordes* in the heart of Mrs Rutherford. The new term has hardly begun and, already, *she is très, très fatiguée....*

She is fatigued because she does not know HOW she will push this class through G.C.S.E.....

● She is fatigued by the increasing numbers of the uninterested & unmotivated in every class.

● She is tired by the stress and aggression. She is FED UP with the shortages of text books. She has had ONE TOO MANY of Paul's absence notes, forged in his Mum's handwriting.

● She is sick of teaching more periods than she is time-tabled for...that, because of *Local Education Authority* cuts in supply teachers, she and her colleagues have to cover for each other when they are ill. She is tired of taking other people's classes, of **humping** projectors all over the school...of the continual lack of time to prepare her own lessons.

Today, Mrs Rutherford *ignores* bad behaviour: supervising detention at the end of the afternoon would mean, yet again, asking someone else to collect her own kids from school...
Elle est tellement démoralisée!
..She feels she never wants to spend another evening marking books ...or another Easter shepherding the school trip to France..... **in fact**, she's going to quit teaching and get a job in public relations.

OH DEAR....
...AU REVOIR

February

The blackbirds bicker nervously in the February dusk. An obese body lies in the library of Blacknest Hall....

"Ooh, blimey!" pants June, the first on the scene. "Oh, it's you...it's Robin! God, you look like **DEATH**," she adds, as the body slowly exhales a deep, **YOGA** breath and begins to adopt a sitting position.

"Yes, one mustn't over-do it," says Robin, an estate agent from Reigate. "Tell me, is my tongue **VERY** coated?"

June, a staff manager for British Home Stores, adjusts her dressing gown. "Face the light a bit...*ooh, yes,* it's **well** wrapped up against the cold! But you expect that, don't you, the first day or so?...You've probably got a **nasty headache,** too, haven't you?"

"Yes..I have...how did you know?" asks Robin, astounded.

"Oh, I'm an old hand at health farms...been to 'em all," she replies. "Must say, I think **Blacknest's** the best".

"I think it's complete **TORTURE!**" sighs Robin. "Can't **WAIT** to go home ...all I've had in the last 3 days is prunes & Bovril".

"**SPECIAL DIET**," observes June, knowledgeably. "Need to lose much?" Robin nods. His G.P. says his heart's under a spot of strain.

"I'm doing **LIGHT DIET,** massage, **RHYTHMIC TRACTION** and **DIA-THERMY**... 'course, I'd like to lose **THESE!**" says June, smacking her thighs. "My **JODHPURS!** ..and I **HAVE** got Irritable Bowel Syndrome too....".

Robin's stomach emits a long, eldritch moan...

OH! SORRY! "Oh, never **MIND!**" laughs June. "You should've heard us in the Women's sauna today! One does get very windy too, didn't you find...in **YOGA** class?"

"It's nice in here," says June, after a pause. "Nice to get away from everybody talking about their insides..."

"All I can think about is **PORK PIES**," says Robin. "I'm **STARVING!**" June licks her lips. "It's **pâté** with me... pâté and cheesecake.... .look, I've got some Maltesers in the car...**ONE** won't hurt... Come on, Robin...Coming?"

Robin gets to his feet, salivating.

MARCH

March's Man of the Month is Antipodean dental practitioner Warren McMurdo.

Here he is trying to control his vexation. The *careous cavity* (lower molar), belongs to Mr Simon Sandercock.

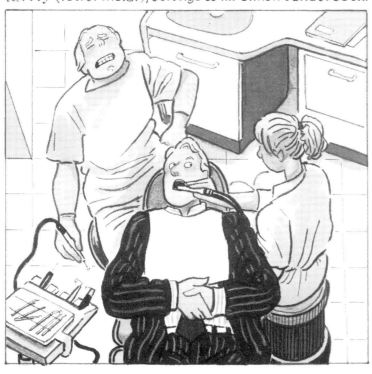

Well, **YOU'D** be flaming **ANGRY**! ..This patient, here, rings first thing..wants an emergency appointment. **GREAT!** He never comes in for **CHECK-UPS**...last time I saw him was before the Wales/France International two years ago.

Our receptionist gives him an O.K. for 10·30. So he turns up an **HOUR** late..waiting room full of people,..**DEMANDS** to be seen...comes in here. puts on an Australian accent....

G'DAY SPORT!

THE NAME'S McMURDO

I get him to open up sharpish and there's this terrible **MESS** of **FOOD DEBRIS** in there...you could grow a crop of mushies... **PLUS** he's got this big cavity. "I'm frightfully sorry, I've come straight from the office ...haven't had time to clean my teeth," he says. So I say, "**I'm** frightfully sorry... **I'VE** come straight from the **TOILET** and haven't had time to wash my hands."
  (Was only kidding. I'm really **HOT** on hygiene. **AND I** wear gloves..I'm not risking **HEPATITIS 'B'**.)
  I usually reckon ½ an hour for a filling ..I give young

Simon a jab..after 10 minutes it still doesn't take - inferior dental nerve block - and I've just been in business with the **DRILL**. Little Simon **CREATES!** Says something really **RIPE** ...with *Denise* sitting there.
  "Gimme another injection!" he says, "and **QUICK!** - I've got a plane to catch..."
  "Yeah. well I got a waiting room of people," I say...and give him the needle...which doesn't take for **20** minutes... and he's lying there frothing about missing this wedding in Scotland....
  And then I'm back to business...and the bloody waterline in me drill **BLOCKS!**... and I'm cleaning it out with fuse wire ..he's **BLASPHEMING** ..and I've got a waiting room of people....
  So. finally I get to fill this **BIGGIE**..and I'm really looking forward to telling him **NOT** to come in here again with such a **DIRTY** mouth, like he's been galloping round a paddock with his **GOB OPEN!** ...And I say to him: OK. now **CLOSE GENTLY**..". and the bastard **CRASHES** his jaws together & **BREAKS** the filling!!....So. I

THE NEXT BIT IS CENSORED. BUT MR SANDERCOCK DID HAVE A PLANE TO CATCH & MR McMURDO, A FULL WAITING ROOM.

April

GIRL of the month is Rachel, (14), seen here, after a poor day at the year's first Gashford Hunt Pony Club One Day Event. She is **BOY MAD**.

PONY of the month is **Sultan**: 14 hands 2 in. 6 yrs. Bay gelding. Hard mouth. Shies at bits of paper. *Absolute* **SWINE** to box, shoe and catch.

FATHER of the month is **Barry**, who has to hump horse boxes all over the shop, when he'd rather be at the Golf Club.

MOTHER of the month is Suki, very out of sorts after a day of shrieking *"Come on, darling... you can do it!"*

*"Yes, I **AM**! Absolutely **LIVID** with you, Rachel! You really let the side down! Don't **EVER** wear earrings with show kit! You **KNOW** it looks **GHASTLY**! You just weren't* **TRYING**, *were you!?* **ALL** *those refusals were* **YOUR** *fault - you look* **DOWN** *all the time! And you kept approaching at* **FAR, FAR** *too tight a turn!*

You made a muck of the dressage.. and, as for pretending **HE** *was lame, so you could go home...* **REALLY**! *I'm* **ASHAMED**! *I mean, most girls'd give their* **EYE-TEETH** *for a penny like Sultan... brand* **NEW** *show saddle.. new sheepskin* **NUMNAH**... *Daddy and me* **HAULING** *out here* **JUST** *for you..* **YOU JUST** *don't* **CARE**, *do you?! You just want to* **STUFF INDOORS** *with that* **IAN**, *don't you!? Well, I've* **HAD IT UP TO HERE**!.. *There's an advert going* **STRAIGHT** *in the paper next week!!!"*

MAY

● HERE'S DIDO, May's darling BUD!
18 years old, a sweet lass of Haverstock Hill & pupil at a private day school.

She's got an accountant father, a solicitor mother. 12 G.C.S.E.s, £100 a month allowance, a place assured at Cambridge and the sort of rosy-eyed, milky-tongued looks that come from following a **STRICT WEEKEND REGIME**

DIET
SATURDAY

1·30 p.m. Wake up
1·35 p.m. Breakfast and Video watching:
   6 oz Coco-Pops
   6 slices bread
   3 pots tea
   8 Marlboro Lights

5-8·00 p.m. Telephoning:
   6 chocolate chip cookies
   6 Marlboro Lights

9·45 p.m. Drinks at Public House:
   5 Vodka limes
   1 Diet Coke
   1 pkt Pork Scratchings
   8 Silk Cut

12·00 a.m. Party in hired room above pub:
   3 Red wine
   2 Perrier waters
   4 drags cannabis
   1 White wine
   3 Silk Cut
   1 Benson and Hedges

3·20 a.m. Shopping at 24 HOUR GARAGE:
   2 Diet Cokes
   1 Twix
   2 Silk Cut

4·00 a.m. SESH at Free House. [i.e. Dido's house. A Free House is one where the parents are away at their weekend cottage].
   Spaghetti
   1 Silk Cut
   1 drag cannabis
   Tap Water

5·30 a.m. Bed.

SUNDAY

2·00 p.m. Wake up

2·05 p.m. Breakfast & T.V. with house guests:
   3 oz taramasalata
   4 slices toast
   3 pots tea

4·00 p.m. Pre-parental return tidying up.
5·00 p.m. House guests depart.

8·00 p.m. Parental dinner:
   Roast lamb
   Potato Gratin, beans
   Fruit Compôte
   Crème fraîche
   2 glasses claret

9·15 p.m. Bed.

NICE EVENING, LAST NIGHT?

MMH... JUST WENT DOWN THE PUB..

JUNE

Etiquette for the New Landed Gintry
Part 6: Dealing with Trespassers

There is no situation more freighted with angst for the new owners of a country place than the intrusion of trespassers upon their property. Traditional respect for *Seignority* allows the **GENTRY** a certain *insouciance* when turfing people off their land, but the **GINTRY**, (*parvenu, novus homo*), must exercise **EXTREME CAUTION**, or else risk appalling loss of face and damage to their social aspirations.

Thus, when you espy a party of trespassers invading

your private fishing, **DO NOT** give voice to your vexation....

This is especially important, if the intruders are dressed in any kind of waxen-wear. From a distance, it is **IMPOSSIBLE** to tell if the wearers are just *Joe Public* in chainstore Barbour-gear, or local **GENTRY** in the *real* thing. Two ill-chosen words to the latter, could utterly **ruin** your ambitions of being welcomed into their social circle.

Have **NO TRUCK**, either, with **ANYTHING** carrying an Ordnance Survey map and wearing fell boots, serious anoraks, Alpine breeches etc.

These people will have **NO** respect for **private ownership** and will make you look foolish when they point out an ancient **Right of Way** on their map.

In both these cases, the **DONE THING** is to remain hidden, whilst your **dog pack** does the harassment. Etiquette demands that your **voice MUST** be heard reprimanding the animals for being *such silly boys.*

You may, however, personally approach any party whose demeanour suggests a **wont** for **forelock-tugging.**

In your most courtly and patrician manner, you may *hint* at the trespass they commit. They will then offer obeisance. This exchange will be satisfying to both sides: they will be giving **you** full endorsement of your new social position. You will give **them** the rich experience of having met a **real**, old-style English **GENTLE PERSON**, such as is rarely to be found beyond the confines of television drama.

July

July's woman of the month is **Gillian Button**, 25 years, 1st class degree in French and Drama, a producer's P.A. at Broadcasting House, earning £9,000 per annum. Gillian is someone who always puts the comfort and wellbeing of others before her own...someone of overwhelming thoughtfulness and consideration....in other words, a **SMOKER**.....

The life of the **SMOKER** is not easy and **GILLIAN** is well used to its sacrificial side....the loneliness, the frustration and, above all, the sense of always being on duty - that one may never smoke **MINDLESSLY**, but always with one's full concentration upon the sensibilities of **OTHERS**.

This solicitude is seen at its most striking at social gatherings, when Gillian's very first utterance will be one of **CONCERN**.....

It is remarkable the sheer **GRACE** with which she will restore the cigarette to its packet and the company to its ease. Remarkable too, is the very great **PERSONAL INCONVENIENCE** to which she must put herself, seeking out those **PERIPHERAL** areas - the edges of crowds, doorways, draughty balconies and fire escapes, empty corridors, **BBC** lavatories ..... where she will hover until her smoking is entirely done.

GILLIAN, however, is as used to **SMOKING** on the fringes of her social life, as she is used to **FUMING** in her humble margin at The Corporation...**FUMING** and chafing in vain for promotion to **RESEARCHER**, as she types the thank you letters to the guests who appeared on the past week's programme.

Happily, for **GILLIAN**, there still exist a few quiet corners, where she and others like her, may mingle, of a lunch hour.

In the bar of **THE GEORGE**, she joins that proud **FREEMASONRY** of **SMOKERS**, each bearing the ancient badges of their habit.... ...the gingery blazes of **AFTERBURN** on the upper lip, the quince-coloured stains on the fingers, the **TAR-BOX BREATH**, the fine Basso-profundo **COUGH-LAUGHS**......

Here, Gillian feels **QUITE** the **DAINTY INGENUE**...a mere **20-A-DAY** girl, with far to go.

AUGUST

Pity **CLIVE TROUTLEY**, (37), August's **MAN OF THE MONTH** .... who has promised that he will re-lay and replace the cork tiles in the utility room, (loosened by a washing machine flood), whilst his wife and children are at Sainsbury's.......

... a man who has just spent an hour in **SLOW MOTION**, before a mirror, propped on a wheelbarrow, in his brown back garden..... where the reflection of the top of his **MAGNIFICENT** back swing has fuelled him with a positively **PLUTONIC OPTIMISM**...

God! You're **LOVELY!**

...a man who has, subsequently, **SLICED** a real shot straight into next door's conservatory.

This man is an **ADDICT** .... whose obsessive habit occupies his every waking hour and is a threat to both his health and his marriage: **CLIVE TROUTLEY** is a **COMPULSIVE GOLFER** ....

As a case, **CLIVE** *suffers all the side-effects* of **SERIOUS ADDICTION** :-

● Tension and anxiety caused by constantly playing **TOPPED BALLS, DUCK HOOKS, SLICES** into the jungle and **DUFF APPROACH SHOTS**.

● Stress, caused by pretending his handicap is 12, when it is really **22**.

● Stress caused by playing the local course, (Par 72), where his fantasies of a round in the 80's are always cruelly shattered.

● Violent mood-swings, when the 'high', of a decent-ish wedge shot is occluded by a muffed putt.

● Self-disgust and the urgent need to re-live the humiliations of a tournament before the glazed and unsympathetic eye of his wife.

● The need to slope off from the office in the lunch hour, to concentrate on his **in-to-out** path at **GOLF CITY**.

● Reckless expenditure on ever better and grander equipment – cavity-backed clubs, personalised golf umbrella, chipping net and fur wood covers taking precedence over the car's new gear box.

This man is sick. He needs serious, **PROFESSIONAL HELP** ....

I AGREE – I'VE JUST ENROLLED FOR A FIVE-DAY INTENSIVE MASTER CLASS AT **GLENCARROCK**

September

When she gets to **W** for **whale**, *something strikes Pippa. She shifts* **Ned** *off her lap and paces up and down the kitchen...*

It's just jolly odd how each picture in the alphabet book, portrays either a **HEALTH HAZARD** *or something threatened with* **EXTINCTION**....

Poor, suspect **apple**, *coated in* **Alar**, *poor* **egg** *and* **ice** *cream, full of salmonella...poor* **COW**, *with its bovine brain disease ...poor, Toxicara-carrying* **Dog**... *poor rabid* **Fox**... *and radioactive* **Lamb**.....

...Poor, threatened **Panda**, **Camberwell Beauty Butterfly**, *and* **Rhino**... *poor* **Tiger**... *poor, sickly* **Seal**, *in its polluted* **Sea**... *poor, wretched* **Whale** ... *poor, extinct* **Quagga**.

There are a number of health hazards in the picture to the left. How many can **YOU** find?

October

There's nothing **FLAKEY** about October's **MAN OF THE MONTH**, ADAM NUBLEIGH (27), except, perhaps, the remains of his tan. There he sits in his little shop, gassing to **SOME WOMAN**, lightly brushing his leg hair, this way and that....

He **SEEMS** to be the product of a **GOOD** school.... and he is! If asked, he makes no secret of the fact that he went to an excellent North London comprehensive.

The stuff he deals in, on the other hand, **IS** highly, and desirably, **FLAKEY**. All his blanket boxes, chests and armoires **SEEM** to be the products of **HONEST CRAFT**, the distressed **SURVIVORS** of a rustic past, worn by **TIME**. And they **ARE**! It's no secret: **SOME** are the **HONEST CRAFT** of the 19th century.... and some the work of his partner, TIM. And they're **ALL** rustic survivors... after the punishment Tim gives them in Suffolk ....

IT'S G.B.H!...ALL THAT STRIPPING, DRY-SCRAPING ...RUBBING..SCUFFING!

BASICALLY, MY STUFF'S EITHER WORN BY TIME ...OR BY **TIM!**...NOT MUCH DIFFERENCE!

His stuff really **sells** at the moment...to St John's Wood and the United States...... But, when the time is right, which could be soon, he'll pull the plug on **FLAKE 'N' SCRAPE JOBS** and wheel out his secret antique investment:

He's got a lock-up garage **FULL** of 1950's Scandinavian and 1960's Inflatables. He's got any amount of stuff in laminated teak and polished alloy.....he's got an entire suite of Quasar **PVC GONFLABLES**... and there's this really amazing **EGG CHAIR**, in sort of ginger leather...... **BEAUTIFUL** stuff... he can hardly wait!

November

November's **WOMAN OF THE MONTH** *is an opera fan. Here,* **NAOMI PADFIELD** *talks all about tonight's performance......*

"Well, it was a performance! You see, we decided to come the **BEACONSFIELD** way and then the **M40**..but the **FOG** was just **GHASTLY**! Traffic really wasn't *too* bad until sort of Northolt-ish...*then* it was almost **GRINDING STANDSTILL** all the way in... couldn't see a **SAUSAGE**..and we both said "Oh **LORD**!"

And then *I* had a brilliant idea! I said to Philip, "Let's have our **NOSEBAG** *now*, while we crawl along!" So, we sat in the *nose-to-tail* and had our opera supper – *Marks and Sparks* sandwiches...**TUNA**, and **VERY GOOD** too!

You see, I always come prepared **NOW**, because Philip's tummy is the absolute **END**! You should've heard it *all* the way through *Così fan tutte*...**WHOLE ARIAS**! *Poor man!* The people sitting next to us...*my dear, if looks could* **KILL**!

Any-way, it was nigh on sevenish, when we got as far as Marylebone Road..I mean, **LONDON TRAFFIC**!! But dear Philip managed some very **CLEVER-CLOGS** stuff...all round the **BACK PASSAGES** ...and, d'you know, we made the foyer by **QUARTER PAST**! Even found a parking place in Lincoln's Inn! I think that was **BRILLIANT**...**VERY** well done! But *what* a performance!!

The opera? Oh, *that was* quite some performance, too! **VERY** well done....."*Peter Grimes*"... frightfully good fog effects ...speaking of which, I think it's **HOME, JAMES**! No, we're not staying to feed our faces...I think it's The Strand for us...Strand, Knightsbridge ...Cromwell Road...then shoot up the **M4**...I think that's our best bet......"

December

COLIN COCKLEY, Managing Director of Retouché Studios, (services to advertising), is MAN of the month. He is seen at the firm's Christmas bash.

WHAT *is* it about jovial COLIN COCKLEY? *Where e'er he walks*, strange things happen to the temperature of the room...people sweat ...go hot and cold.......

He has only to raise a sober glass of *Aqua Libra* to one of his swaying *confrères* and to say, brightly:......

WELL, CHEERY WEARIES, ALAN... HAPPY CHRISTMAS!

...to get Jonathan's forefinger drumming at his shirt buttons, like a woodpecker.....

I BIN WITH THIS ✳✳✳ING FIRM FIVE ✳✳✳✳ING YEARS..AN' YOU STILL DON'T KNOW MY ✳✳✳✳ING NAME!

And when Mick asks if Colin's doing anything special for Christmas and Colin says "Oh, nothing much...just home, with Helen and the kids," Natasha gets into a right MUCK SWEAT.

SHE and Colin have been doing *something special* almost every day between 6 o'clock and 7.... not to mention, an hour ago in the Dark Room.

Across the room, Sophie's feeling hot and cold and shivery.

A-TISHOO!

This time last year, she and Colin did special things...and she gave him a Christmas present, that's still locked in his office desk. But there are no hard feelings now....In a moment, she'll go and give him a big, festive hug. Sophie's still got flu...and, who knows, perhaps Colin will spend his Christmas feeling hot and cold and shivery too......

Bumping *along the bottom*

Bumping along the BOTTOM

Here is Miles Upmaster, *ex* reinsurance broker, *ex* dealer with U.S. surplus lines ...NOW *surplus* himself...victim of the shrunken market...casualty of a company merger reshuffle....

WHAT he'd give **NOW** to be peddling *Italian Personal Accident*, or, even *Moroccan Motor XL's*.... **HOW** he'd **GIVE** his back legs to be spoofing for lunch at The Marine Club....instead of spending the day **DEALING**....

..dealing with *tide-marks*... dealing with dog hair...

...dealing with the stinky flower water...

Pwah!

..dealing with the aroma of freshly made coffee..

...before dealing with the arrival of the girl from the estate agents with another lot of PROSPECTIVE buyers...

This is Mr & Mrs Vole

Hi

...which means dealing with a rush of impotent **RAGE**......

o yeah?

...as they cruise round the house, avoiding eye-contact... with their bloody, **SMUG, SUCKS-TO-YOU-IT'S-A-BUYERS' MARKET** expression...aiming their camcorder at the most sensitive and private parts.....

It means dealing with a routine surge of **BILE** and **NAUSEA**....

No..don't think they're interested

MIGHT be worth your dropping the price another **twenty K**...

..It means controlling a terrible, *hysterical* impulse to **SCREAM**:

OK...Wull...um...

GODSAKE!! BUY MY BLOODY HOUSE!!!

MAY NOT LOOK DESERVING.. BUT IN DEEP FINANCIAL SHITE...MARRIAGE CRACKING UP... NEVER FIND ANOTHER JOB ..GETTING AN ULCER..CAN'T SLEEP P-L-E-A-S-E MAKE ME LIQUID!!

Cheers then

Cheers

God, **HOW** I need to kick-start my economy....

© Posy Simmonds 1992

Election FEVER (Convalescence)

The children escaped it..

...Dan said he was immune...

..I had it for THREE WEEKS!! ...the LOW-LEVEL kind..you just feel QUEASY and depressed all the time... it affects your EYES, too...

...and, sometimes, you'd get these VIOLENT attacks of NAUSEA in the street....

Early morning, you felt WORST:

I thought my husband would be all right.. ..but on THURSDAY night, he went down with the 24 HOUR kind....

..It started with this terrible GRIPING...

And then, he was up and down ALL NIGHT with it....pouring sweat... ..raging thirst for information...

And Dan got it too..he was as SICK as a parrot in the early hours....

Next day, James was as fit as a flea...

...whilst I had this terrible LINGERING HEADACHE.

© Posy Simmonds 1992

*...The moment of the Arrival of the **GREAT HERDS**..that moment when the wide, silent, empty concourses begin to fill with ungulates...lowing, grazing, cud-chewing, casting their droppings as they claim their ancestral shopping-grounds.*

*That this sight still survives is a miracle: **YEARS** of economic drought have devasted the once lush malls...and the herds, themselves, are decimated by fiscal murrain and the predations of hungry creditors.....*

Against all the odds, one of the world's Great Natural Sights still survives......

*Most of these gentle, docile creatures seem unaware of the **THREATS** to their numbers and to their habitat.....*

...and only one or two seem to sniff the wind in alarm...

*Not much is known about these animals, particularly in **LIFE-STYLE** threatening situations. It is thought that they **SENSE** the precipice edge, over which **GROUP-HYSTERIA** would send them plummeting...*

This is one of Nature's mysteries, ...one which may never be unravelled

TOPPED BALLS

Here are FIVE people leaving the last hole of the Royal Chipworth Golf Course *in an unutterably FILTHY temper...*

JAMES has just accused ME of ruining his chances of getting membership here!

I've done NOTHING!

Never mind MY plans!.. HE wanted the children kept out of the way, while he played... *I've* spent HOURS hanging about this bloody golf course!

We were so *patient*... we had a walk... we found all these *WILD MUSHROOMS*... we waited and waited...

Yet it was HIS turn to look after the kids!

He KNEW I had a meeting...he KNEW I needed the car...he took NO notice...

I don't matter— BLOODY GOLF always comes first!

Sophie's behaviour has been quite MONSTROUS!!!

SHE, unilaterally, draws up a *draconian* rota of domestic duties...and to HELL with my few, precious hours of recreation!

Bloody despot!

She's made me *slice* my balls all afternoon.... with her muttering and watch-tapping and SHRIEKING that she's found *mushrooms*....

Look! Boletus!

...and her jumping out, when I'm addressing a 40 foot putt, waving DEATH CAPS at me....

LOOK!

...she *severely* embarassed me in front of Nobby...

GOD! HOW much longer?!

When old Crouch asked me to put him up for membership here, I TOLD him the Committee would take his WIFE'S attitude into account...

You see, we *like* the wives to FIT IN...to take an interest in their spouses' game..and *not* to begrudge the time their husbands spend on the course...

...and we expect them to take an ACTIVE part in the Club's social life...organising DINNER DANCES, raffles..tombolas and so on...

..but a *resentful* wife, like Mrs Crouch..a wife who maliciously spoils her husband's *birdie opportunities*...who is the wanton cause of *soaring slices* and *duffed approach shots*...

HURRY UP!!!

...a woman, moreover, who seems intent on feeding her husband *poison* mushrooms... ...who has the air of *Lucretia Borgia*.......

...and who lurks like some mad, feminist *Flasher*.... comes WAY below *par* in my book....

© Posy Simmonds 1992

Terminal Belly Ache

flight SHOP

Shall I buy you a paper, my sweetheart, ...magazine?

Oh, OK

Departures

Come on! Come on!

God! This bloody ...**FILTHY** culture!

?

I can't take it!

LOOK what it does to people! **LOOK** at the bastards!

They live on **JUNK**! ..watch it..read it ...eat it!

They're coaglums of **JUNK**!!

Bloody **PLAY-PEN** culture! ..big **BABIES** in their play clothes ...half-hourly feeds of **SUGAR**!

..breath *stinking* of **E NUMBERS**...

Kids full of rotting little *milk teeth*!

..and **what** they fill their **MINDS** with!

Violence! Gossip!

Sex-sludge!

Regurgitated **TELLY-PAP!**

They're all brain-dead... **MORONS**!

MENTAL COSTIVES!

It's all right... It's OK..

..he's a writer- he's always like this when he can't see any of his novels on the bookstall...

Déjeuner sur le PATIO

It's extraordinary how one's sensory responses are heightened when one is in rural FRANCE

Sitting beside the pool of one's renovated farmhouse, sipping a PASTIS, the sun high over the vineyards, one is gripped by an overwhelming feeling of.....

God! This is HELL!

Absolute Purgatory!

Look, it's the NOISE! ...the STINK! ...the POLLUTION...the hostile environment...the CLAUSTROPHOBIA!

It's unbearable!

The STINK! Pwuuf! It's Methane – septic tank's blocked AGAIN...bloody French plumbers never put enough traps in the system

And POO! Chlorine! This ruddy pool... s'either full of lethal SLIME or chemicals!

STINKS!

we're exposed to more toxic substances in a MONTH here, than a YEAR in London....

..what with the copper sulphate, when they spray the vines....

But the POOL!

God...the chlorine tablets! – big ones, you pass out from the fumes...little ones fizz..bloody burn your hands!

And, while they're doing their stuff, you have to run the filter pump for 48 hours...the NOISE! ...the FORTUNE in electricity!

And when you finally get to use the pool, the water really knackers your skin..all raw bits on your finger tips..in your body creases. ...your eyes get bloodshot...

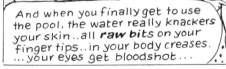

And the sense of being under siege, here....

Us, and one or two Dutch and Belgians, we're the only ones who don't vote for Le Pen, who don't have steel shutters and 7 foot grille fences, to keep out the arabes voleurs....

And the CLAUSTROPHOBIA! We're hemmed in...if you walk, you get eaten by massive dogs....

...or electrocuted in the terrains piégés – booby-trapped land.. ...wired to mains electricity!

You see all one wants is the simple life...a little corner of sun-drenched brick..balmy air...a place where you find the best olives.. ..fresh thyme..basil..excellent wines.... charming little restaurants...

Ah..Hampstead!

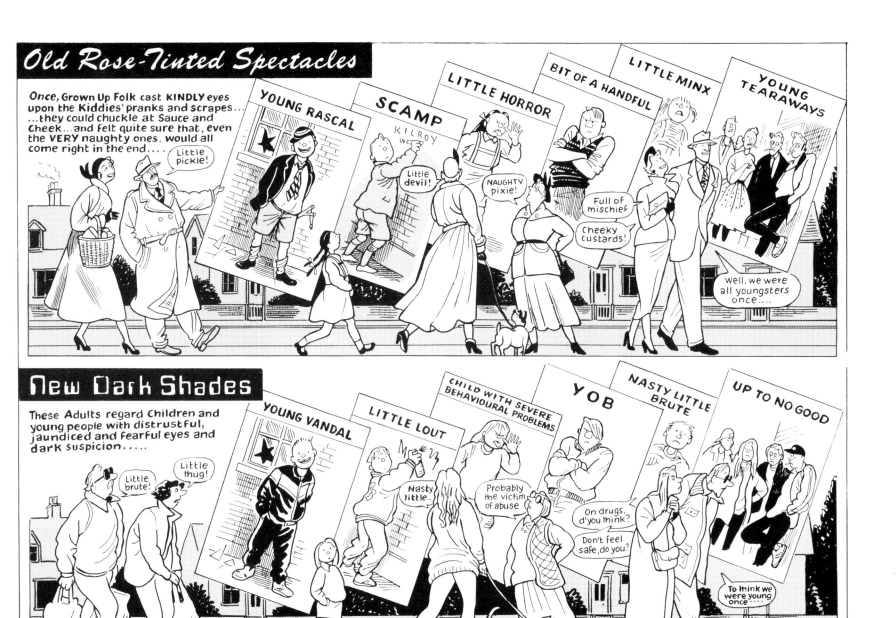

The Brood

Oh **Mum**! You **WOULDN'T**! That's **sick**..really **sick**!

You're **PAST** it, Mum!..biologically past it.......

I'm not saying I **WOULD**... but the technology's there... I saw a thing on telly.... -mothers at **50**...**55**, even..

I love little babies...

But you had **US**!

Anyway, it's **SICK**!

What's **sick**?

You! Your age group...

...you refuse to accept you're **old** and past it...

...'s really **GROSS**..women having babies when they're practically **geriatric**!

SICK!

GROSS!

SELFISH!

Just older **WOMEN**? What about old **MEN** having babies?

That sick too?

Yeah.. old blokes, too.. **well** sick! **REVOLTING**!

Why **revolting**?... you mean, old people shouldn't... **mate**?

Eeuch! No, they shouldn't!

GROSS!

's not just that, Mum... ...it's sort of sick generationally

I don't want to go into **Mothercare** and find it full of **pensioners** and their **newborn**...

..and racks of Mothercare **zimmers** and **trusses**

Anyway, you old people have such crap ideas...

..about **OUR** music, computer games 'n' stuff

...'s **SICK**...**more** kids being brought up with your prejudices...

Yes, your generation thinks it's bloody **immortal**.... you just want to go on perpetuating your horrible **1960**'s culture into the next century....

But it's **OUR** turn now!

You lot should just sit back and be **PROPER** grandparents ...**I** don't want you saying to Maudie "Sorry, Granny can't play hide and seek... she's gone into labour...

..and I don't want you asking her to help change **uncle**'s nappy...

No, you should be helping **US**...babysitting..child-minding when I find a job... or when we want a holiday on our own...

You should be thinking of **US**...**OUR** children... You should be shelling out for insurance policies for their education....

You should be seeing **us ALL RIGHT**, after you peg out...

Leave us a nice big house...

Ooh **GROSS**!

SELFISH..!

P.C.* P.C. 43

*Politically Correct

A law enforcement executor,
Called P.C. 43
Is a model of Correctness and
New Objectivity...

In dealing with the Public,
His vocabulary confirms
Preference for unprejudiced and
Non-judgmental terms

"FAT"..."OLD"...."SHORT".."MAD"...
He's all for their removal,
HE chooses words that don't imply
A sense of Disapproval....

Unstigmatised, unbranded,
How NICE the world might be...
If we were all as P.C.
As P.C. 43

© Posy Simmonds 1992

© Posy Simmonds 1993

The Perfect Present

Here is a woman looking for a suitable present for two nice little girls, one aged ten, the other, nine....

...the daughters of her boy-friend, who will come for Christmas, while their mother holidays in Luxor with her lover.....

Here is a woman who is **FURIOUS** *with her boy friend's ex-wife...*

SHE was the guilty party...but she got the house.. the Volvo..bloody generous child maintenance...

she's **always** going on holiday with her **rich** bloke...leaving the kids at Paul's

..He can only afford a *tiny* little flat...

..She really took him to the cleaners ...God, she's a....

Here is a woman who's found the **PERFECT** *present for the two little girls.. JUST what they'd* **LOVE**...*Junior* **KARAOKE**, *with* mini **AMPLIFIERS** *and* echo/voice mix **RADIO MICROPHONE**.....*

Cor! You're going to have a **noisy** Christmas!

I know!

This is a woman, who will now go to her boyfriend's cramped little flat, to help make everything nice for the impending visit....

...but who knows, if it's any-thing like **LAST** *year, all* **HER** *efforts will be met with cold indifference by the two little girls.....*

Look! Maggie's made a **SNOWMAN** cake!...**Look!**

we know

She knows that Paul will get displays of extravagant and ex-clusive affection.....

...whilst **SHE** *will get vented on her, all the repressed* **RAGE** *and resentment, they feel about their parents' break-up.....displays of sulks, truculence and wilfully revolting table manners....*

But, since **when** are you vegetarian? ..you liked turkey last year...

She **hated it** last year!

...and, whilst she anticipates that, in her presence, the **Junior KARAOKE** *will be grudgingly unwrapped and then pointedly ignored .....*

Don't you want to have a go with it?

No... later on

...she knows it'll have a **TREMENDOUS SUCCESS**, *once it goes home!*

Darlings..look, we've got terrible jet-lag...

Maggie gave it us!...it's **Wicked!**

© Posy Simmonds 1992

I'm dreaming of a....

...really, really super Christmas...

Let us dream along with *Options trader, Alistair Razer-Dorke & his wife, Belinda, (née Weber), the director of Canapé Express [bespoke party food]......*

*If **YOU** were in their shoes, where would you like to spend the Festive Season? Would you, for instance, be thinking of staying with **HER** people...?*

THE VENUE:

Hi!

Victorian terrace house, late 60's conversion. One kips on a futon in the sitting room; one eats in the basement kitchen-diner; atmosphere rather febrile and foetid, owing to many siblings, broken extractor fan, proximity of cat tray, guinea pig cage and high consumption of fags and garlic.

THE MENU:

Sparkling Blanc de Blancs
Borscht
Garlic bread
Supermarket Best Buy:
Côtes de Gascogne
Roast turkey with
lentil & chestnut
stuffing
Potato cakes
Aubergine purée
Her Dad's Figgy Pud
Crème Fraîche
Calvados

THE CONVERSATION:

*I mean, **what is** this country coming to!!?* — **I GIVE UP!** — All those boorish ministers going on about **CHOICE**, as if everyone had the means to choose...

She's made a society which just values **MONEY**.... — ..if it doesn't pay, **CUT** it!.... — The poor just subsidise the **RICH**!

Things couldn't be worse — **A CRUEL society** — It may be a bloodless revolution, but it's death by 1,000 cuts!

---

*Or, would one prefer to go to **HIS** people?*

Hallo, darlings!

THE VENUE: Perfectly decent country house, allowed to rot into a **COMPLETE TIP**, set in 9 acres of bramble. *Interior:* dark, damp, draughty, mothy and pungently **DOGGY**. *Underfoot:* the constant crunching of myriad bluebottle corpses.

Tinky! STOP Scratching!

Now, what's your poison?

THE MENU

Lady Curzon cocktail
(with a few maraschino
cherries, found in the
pantry cupboard)
· Melon
(with ditto cherries)
· Incinerated pheasants
· Crisps· Bread sauce
· Khaki Brussels sprouts
Ch. Mouton d'Armailacq
1934 (foully oxidised)
· Christmas Pud
(bought at the W.I.
donkey's years ago)
· Stilton
· Port

THE CONVERSATION:

I mean, what **IS** the country coming to?! — It's all so ghastly! — I mean, why have I got to wait 18 months to get my knee done? In the old days, there weren't these QUEUES! I don't dare walk in that precinct...all those yobboes and peculiar people hanging about.....

 Everyone's just money-mad! All these rich people buying up the village..! — No bus service now ...so my daily just can't get here... ...it's so **GHASTLY**... — Going to the dogs ..going to the dogs

---

..Or, perhaps, one will just stay at home...

THE VENUE: Two bedroom, waterfront, duplex apartment, with security-controlled, undercover parking, porterage and video entryphone.....

Le Menu

Apéritif
Champagne Brut de Krug

Salade Tiède
de cuisses de grenouilles

Montrachet Criots-Bâtard 1984

Roast Capon
Mazy-Chambertin Joseph Roty 1982

Les Fromages

Compotier de fruits confits
Vin de Paille Hermitage

THE CONVERSATION:

Absolutely the right descision to stay here.. All that **moan-moan-moan** from everyone every-where....... — **What is** the country coming to?

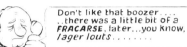

© Posy Simmonds 1988

Christmas: The Adoration of the General Public

The end of **January** 1989

The end of January

From a distance, the little hamlet of Tresoddit, reposing in its out-of-season calm, seems unchanged: there is not much sign, as yet, of the new Marina Complex... and the "Non-Estate" housing development is screened by the bosky slopes of Bolscudda Hill.

The grey swells still heave against the mole as ever, and the black-headed gulls wheel and shriek like a Sioux raiding party, above the sewage outfall.....

But, from the threshold of his shop, this warm January day, Kevin Penwallet gazes upon a scene of VIOLENT upheaval: They are tearing out the old sewers in Tresoddit.....

As Tresoddit prospers in the LEISURE BOOM, as it expands and builds, as its tourist population soars, its poor, worn, Victorian digestive system simply CANNOT COPE: the bay is a SINKHOLE of untreated sewage and the local beaches, all well over the limit of 2,000 FOECAL COLIFORMS, have utterly failed the E.E.C. SAFE BATHING STANDARD...

However, in future...a screening plant at Tregodnoze Head will remove the INDISSOLUBLE matter and discharge the remaining effluent down new-laid pipelines out to sea.

Kevin Penwallet muses upon all the sewage that has flowed past his shop in the last decade... and feels that, in some way, HE is now like the effluent of the future, that HE has been "TREATED," and has become LESS of a POLLUTANT to the local community than he was in the late 1970s, when he returned to his native village and created a terrible STINK....

1979: Ex-anthropology lecturer, Penwallet zealously transformed the local grocer shop, from an outlet of processed factory-fare, into a CORNUCOPIA of wholesome and ecologically sound nutrition...

This enterprise was deemed to be a LOAD OF CRAP by local and visitor alike... and Kevin, himself was considered a.....

Only his ex-polytechnic colleague, GEORGE WEBER, had a kind word.....

1985: Penwallet is forced to bow to the chill economic climate and his own near bankruptcy. Unable, because of cuts in higher education, to reclaim a living in Academia, he is obliged to lower his sights...and, thus becomes yet ANOTHER purveyor of LAVENDER BAGS, FLORAL OVEN GLOVES, MOB-CAPPED JAMS, SICKLY FUDGES, CERAMIC FAUNA and INDUSTRIAL ICE CREAM....

The less discerning visitors thought this reincarnation SUPER... -perhaps not on a par with National Trust shops - but VERY SWEET all the same.....Kevin's tills rang and rang.

The LOCALS thought it STANK ...as did George Weber and Kevin, himself.....

1988: Penwallet turns his shop into an up-market delicatessen. He and his partner, ROZ, a professional cook, offer the increasing numbers of affluent visitors and residents a variety of epicurean delights, specialising in those delicacies, which the nearest Marks & Spencers does not yet provide. The shop is a wild success and is soon listed in guide books and magazines. His clientele adore Kevin... and even those impecunious locals are pleased that he has put Tresoddit on the map as a centre of excellence...

Only George Weber sniffs:

1989: Soon the breezes of Tresoddit will smell as sweet as Kevin's name. Soon the sewage will be pumped out to sea... and, just as Kevin feels distanced from his qualms of conscience, so Tresoddit will feel well away from its noxious discharge....

...Perish the thought, that the economic tide should turn, and some ill wind hurl back foul effluvia upon our hero's bright present....

The end of **February**

Oh no, Tamsin...you're not buying *that*, are you?

Owh, **DAD!**

What's she buying? ...not more rude willy cards?

No..something **much** more **potent**...

...*entre nous*, she bought one of **these**....

Aah! Dear Tammy! How **sweet!**

Yes, it *is* sweet...'

To Mother...

...but *isn't* it also rather **depressing**...? I mean, Wendy... look around..all these Mothers' Day cards...

Doesn't anything strike you?

Isn't it *odd* that the only **senti-mental** images of **mothers** are a **hundred** years old..... Literally a **100** years on these...

See..here: any number of **19th** century genre paintings..... And here's **Renoir**... **Monet**... **Mary Cassatt**.....

...or, look at the modern ones... Smallish animals, dressed up in **Victoriana**...

Hmm...yes..very *sweety-poo*...

To Mummy

Happy Mother's Day!

We-ell..it's just cosy **nostalgia**...

Yes! Nostalgia for cosy mothers: demonstrably domestic, dependent, non-**voting**, non-**smoking**.....non-trouser-wearing and not on the **PILL**...like *secular* **MADONNAS**...

THIS century can't make **mothers** look so **comforting**...

There's the **1940s** & **50s**, of course

We're nostalgic for **THEM**....

They're busy **refabricating** those years as **telly** drama... Ads...fashion...

"...penurious, war-time hearths...**Fair Isles**.... wirelesses..mothers in pinnies doling out **Milk of Magnesia**...."

We desperately **NEED** even **parody** images of the time when **MOTHER** was infinite-ly domestic...**never mind** the horrors of the old poverty...or the War...

..The **1920's** myths aren't any use...cocktails and eman-cipation...nor are the **1960s** - drugs and revolution.... same with the seventies...

And it's because we're a **FRIGHTENED** society! We want **MUMMY!**

Nothing's **SAFE** any more!

..Streets are full of **muggers**..addicts.. ..child molesters...**countryside's** full of **radio active** sheep..cows with **brain-rot**...**rivers & seas** are full of **JUNK**...the **ozone** layer's ruptured... **Nothing's** safe to **EAT**...**Sex** is **DANGEROUS**...

..and here we are, fumbling our way in the dark towards the new century...and we want **Mummy's** hand to hold... even if she's a ruddy **bear** in a **dirndl!**

I hope you're **not** suggesting you **like** the picture of women walled up in their homes?

No, No! Certainly **not!**..but I have in mind...well..an **up-to-date** version of Tamsin's card...

...it's just that it would look like... a **child minder's**.....

The end of **March:** — *Memory Lanes*

Wads of **TISSUE FLOWERS** star the verges with bursts of pink, blue, white and yellow....

The sun catches the glossy bells of **BITTERLOUT** and **GOLDEN PEE** ..... or "*Snort Shells*," as quaint countryfolk would have them .....

We city folk have so little time to stand and stare...and so, what **GREATER** joy at Eastertide than to roam the Springtime **LANES**...................

Lulled by the drowsy hum of idling motors, we amble, ears a-prick and eyes a-glint, **GOBSTRUCK** by Nature's Marvels, bedecking verge and bank and wayside shoulder....

The lane banks are gay with **DROPFOIL**, ...**GUMBANE** and **YELLOW CORN COCKLE**...

...and in lay-by nooks, colonies of **BUFF-TIPPED LUNG BUTTS** are breeding.....

Here, also, we find the first shy **CONDOMS** peering through the grasses...waxy gold or translucent pink. Country folk know them as "**GOBLINS' FINGERSTALLS**", or "**JACK-BE-QUICK**", and old wives hold they ward off ill luck.

I'M NOT interested **WHAT** it **IS**... **WILL** you get back in the car this minute!

On inner lane-side shoulders, there are other creatures to espy... There's **OLD BROCK**... basking in his final slumber...

Oh God! **DON'T LOOK!** Squashed badger! · **HORRIBLE**! Agh!

"The fewer his years, the fewer his tears," is a wise old country saying.

Merry **CROWS** are refecting upon this tipsy-cake of carrion. Country lore says "The folly of one is the fortune of another."

Up on the hillside the farmer goes about his timeless toil...

Spraying bloody **POISONS**! **Think** of all those **NITRATES** leaching into the water supply!

We've got to **EAT** all that **TOXIC** crap!

But, as the old saw has it: "Everyman must eat a peck of dirt before he dies."

The **KESTREL** would agree, as he eyes our gentle progress down the lanes. Also known as the **MERCURY** bird, his liver is rich in **ORGANO-CHLORINE** residues.....

The **LAMBS** are a-gambol in the meadows, and by quaint farmsteads, the **CALVES** are calling for their dams.....

I stopped eating **MEAT**...it's all radioactive or full of hormones

I read in The Guardian that calves are fed chocolate-flavoured **PIGS' BLOOD**!

O God! No!

But "Hungry dogs will eat dirty puddings," is a wise old country saw.

From our lane, we scent the nearby river, where the sun gleams on the alabaster flanks of myriad **FISH**, lying at anchor in the snuff-coloured foam. "Cast not out foul water till you bring in the clean", and "Better dead fish than empty dish", are old proverbs...

And now our ramble's abruptly done: A wagon blocks our lane...and there's a sodium hydrosulphide flood no foot can ford...

...But, as country folk well know," Every path hath a puddle."

We weep by the wayside.........

Been here **2 HOURS**!

TOXIC load! I mean. **WHAT'S** it **DOING** on the road, for **CRYING OUT LOUD**!?!?

We remain unconsoled by that oft-said saw: "Nothing dries sooner than a tear."

The end of **April**

Hello...

Um...well...I just wanted to say something **POSITIVE** about **THINGS** today...'cos, I mean I **DO** think **SOMEONE**'s got to say it....

.'cos just about **everyone** goes on about how **GHASTLY** Life's become in Britain over the past ten years...

..I'm **NOT** saying it's **ALL** **hunkydory**..but I do think there **ARE** things to feel optimistic about....

...Speaking as I find, **I FEEL** people are more **CARING**, more **neighbourly**...and our **PEACE OF MIND**'s a jolly sight greater than it was in 1980!

..I mean, take this street : it used to be **really GROTTY** when we were first here...people **didn't CARE** about their houses ...the shops were **ALL** rundown....

...But, gradually, people who **DID care** moved in...they improved the houses...the shops looked up.....**NOW**, you can buy **EVERYTHING**, from **prosciutto** to pink fir apples..... ...I call that **REAL** progress!

And,...see that tiny bit of open ground out there? **THAT** was just a sort of **DUMP**!

HORRIBLE, whirly-eyed **DOSSERS** used it - **quite AWFUL!** I can't **TELL** you!...They used to pee all over our viburnums!

So...**WE** and other like-minded souls, we pressured the council...got the **TRAMPS** moved on..got it cleaned up...we **reclaimed** it for the whole community!

Now, it's a little urban Nature Reserve ...we've sown it with wild Flowers.... and we get **super** butterflies !

You see, **I see that** as an example of people **CARING**, working together...... **Community spirit !**

Well, we're **ALL** carers in this street..

Especially **US!**..we even care for the **OLD**..Simon's aunt lives downstairs in the basement.

You **see**, we're responsible as **INDIVIDUALS**...because that's part of the **challenge!**

You just **can't** lie back and ask the **State** to provide everything...you've got to **WORK** for things !

I know Simon and I feel a terrific **buzz** of achievement that we can afford the **best** for our children...the **best** schooling..medicine... ...**and a SECURE home**, too, of course.....

..And, my God, it **IS** secure! We've spent a **MINT** on **SECURITY**: locks, floodlighting...150 decibel sirens... sensors...all wired up to the local cop shop..We're like **Fort Knox**!

Well, it's **PEACE** of **MIND**... ..such **ghastly** people about

We kitted up **Aunty** with one of those **alarm** thingies you wear on your wrist - **such a boon**, as it was an **AWFUL BORE** having to go down and see how the old bag was...

Now, we don't have to bother

But, providing a **SECURE** home's **so** important..if the **worst** happened. we've got **SIX** panic buttons...

...and Simon keeps an electric **pig prod** by the bed...chums in the country gave it to us... it's for herding animals...

Actually, Simon says he's **DYING** to give a burglar a few **squillion volts** in the **arse !!!!**

Well, it's **peace** of **mind**, isn't it ?

EE-AH-EE-AH!

GOD ALMIGHTY!

what's **THAT**?

EEE-AH-EE-AH!

Oh no..it's O.K... ..**PANIC** over!

EE-AH-AH!

It's only **Aunty's screecher!** ...Probably means she's fallen over the dog.....

..Now, **where** was I .....?

The end of **May**: "Jerusalem"

And did these brogues in ancient times
Walk upon Nigel's verdant sward?

...Or, were they on-ly just acquired
In Bond Street with an Access card?

And did those ads of Ralph Lauren's
Convert us swine to classy pearls?

And was our greatest aim in Life
To look and live like landed earls?

Ackchee, **don't** look **TOO** hard at the house...we're still in **SUCH** a **Shambles...!**

Contractors are **s'posed** to finish the **balustrading** and **basket weave** paths **NEXT** week...then, hopefully, they get cracking on the new conservatory...

Meanwhile, **I** just spend my **whole** life choosing paints and fabrics...

we thought **ALL tartan** for the library...gun metal stucco walls... Victorian **servants' staircase** wall-paper for the dining room...

But, honestly, don't **ask** me about the other rooms...just haven't the foggiest yet....

It's all such a **palaver**... just **PRAY interest rates** don't go on **zooming** up......

Bring me no tales of woeful dearth!
Spare me your pleas for charity....

...I don't yet wish to Save the Earth,
Till I have built my orangery......

I cannot curb my lust to spend,
Nor can my card sleep in my hand...

Darling.... Wouldn't this do for the dining room?

...Till I've built MY Jerusalem,
In England's green and pleasant land!

© Posy Simmonds 1989

The end of **June:** *Our Friendly Neighbourhood*

© Posy Simmonds 1989

The end of **July:** *Turning back the Floral Clock*

1959:

Remember when this was just a little municipal garden...with a **FLORAL CLOCK** covered in lolly sticks, bottle tops and dog ends? There were one or two palms, Clock Golf, a string of fairy lights and a caff that shut at 5·30 p.m.

Well, *REALLY!* It's a public *disgrace!*

Dreary little God forsaken dust heap!

I mean, holiday-makers expect something a bit more **LIVELY!**

Bugger all to do in the evenings

God, it's **DIRE!**

Remember the TEDS?

Hooligans desecrate floral clock

Holiday makers watched in alarm last night, as a gang of Rock 'n' Roll crazed louts caused £600 worth of damage to the sea front Pleasure Garden. The gang wrecked palms and plants, smashed fairy lights and were seen to commit nuisances upon the floral clock.

In a statement, Councillor Roy Twiss (42), said "This was an act of wanton, malicious, vandalism by criminal young thugs, with no respect for public property."

There's talk of **BIRCHING**, isn't there...?

Yes, well, it's a pretty pass, when **DECENT FAMILY FOLK** can't enjoy a civic amenity without being intimidated by **DELINQUENTS!**

They say it's **BOREDOM** to blame, don't they? No **Facilities** for the young...**nothing** for them to do....It's **FRUSTRATION...ALIENATION**...those poor no-hopers in dead-end jobs...

Something ought to be done!

1969:

Remember when it became The Funarama and they put security railings round the floral clock...and there was a disco, slot machines, a burger bar, pin ball, three souvenir shops, and a Krazy Golf course...?

It's a public disgrace!

An *eyesore!*

The **NOISE!**

The **STINK!** Onions! grease! Dog poo!

Mod v Rocker clash destroys floral clock

Terrified holiday makers gazed in horror as violence broke out between gangs of Mods and Rockers at the Funarama on Tuesday. In running battles, where bricks and bottles were thrown, the floral clock was destroyed, deck chairs burnt and shop windows smashed.

Estimating the damage done to be over £2,000, Cllr. Roy Twiss, (52), said, "This is an outrage of senseless violence by sick young layabouts. They should all be birched."

It's a pretty pass, when **DECENT, ORDINARY FOLK** are subjected to scenes of violence by gangs of **LOUTS** and **DROP OUTS**

But, it's **ANGER** they feel! **ANGER**...

...and FRUSTRATION with our sick, materialistic society!

1979:

Remember when they redeveloped the site into the Jubilee Arcade? ...an Aladdin's cave, full of Space Invaders, set in area of skate board ramps, a pizza bar and 2 disco pubs...all police patrolled.

JUBILEE ARCADE

Evening Post **ANIMALS!** SKINHEADS RIOT IN ARCADE MAYHEM

Horrible young **THUGS!**

Good birching wouldn't do them any harm!

Birching won't solve anything!

IT'S SOCIETY that's sick...the **UNEMPLOYMENT**......

Oh, **BELT UP!**

1989:

Now, it's a fully fortified **FAMILY LEISURE ATRIUM**...with: **SUPA**-Cinema, **WHIRL-WAVE** pool, **ice rink**, **BRASSERIE**, **CROISSANTERIE**, Food Court and Boutique **VILLAGE**; a computer-controlled environment, 24 hour security surveillance, State-of-the-Art **GUARD DOG PATROL** and **BIG BROTHER**-Electronic Card **ENTRY/EXIT** control system.....

It's *horribly* clean...

Horrible atmosphere... ..eerie..you know you're being watched...

And the **PRICES!**

It's consumerism gone mad!

You know there's a **RIOT** going on outside?

Is there!?

Well, what d'you expect? ...it's those poor, young people...some can't afford to come in here ...and some they won't let in....

Nothing else for 'em to do...except get drunk....

Poor things!...I remember when **FUN** didn't cost anything...

Remember the nice little garden, used to be here...? With that Floral Clock..?

Aah. Yes

Lovely, wasn't it?

Oh..**wish** we could put the **clock** back....

The end of **August:**

© Posy Simmonds 1989

The end of **September:** *A Jeremiad for the new Academic Year*

As performed by Senior Polytechnic Staff and Course Co-ordinators.

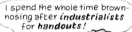

© Posy Simmonds 1989

The end of **October:**

"My God!"

"You've **sold** it!!?"
"Yup!"

AT LAST! After **18** months of **complete TORTURE!!**

"So...what did you get for it?"

"**GET** for it!? What did we **GIVE**'s more like it!"

"Cost us a bloody **FORTUNE!**"

"**NEVER** try and sell your house! People **SCREW** you **RIGID!!**"

I mean, you put it on the market...and... first, they stay away in **DROVES**....

Then the agent suggests dropping the asking price...so we knock off **15** grand..

Then you get **dribs** and **drabs** of people **SNIFFING** round....

"At **ALL HOURS!**"

...totally **KNACKER** yourself rushing back from work.... cleaning up....

...Extractor fan going **night & day** 'cos the **au pair** just **WILL NOT** go into the garden to **smoke**....

...and the children **NEVER** flush the loo after them!

...And these **PEOPLE**, they just **cruise** through your house in **2 minutes**, with their **video cameras**:

...and then go home and have a good laugh, as they replay your **damp patches**...and **you**, madly flushing and apologising.....

"So **SORRY!** Our 5 year old..."
"Always forgets!"

IMAGINE! Year and a half of **THAT!** Anyway, these **LEECHES** have finally bought it...

...and, **GOD!**

"**Did** they **MUCK** us about!"

First, they make us drop another **ten thousand**...

"No!"

...then they **faffed** around.....

...so we were forced to offer them the **entire** contents of our kitchen.. **BRAND NEW** fridge-freezer, **microwave** – you **name** it!......

"God!"

"And **STILL** they wouldn't **SIGN!**"

What clinched it was when we offered them **2 years**' worth of **opera tickets** that Hamish gets on the firm...**plus**, they made us pay for their **survey**....

"**Ffwooo!**"

EXTORTIONISTS! BLOODSUCKERS!!

The **GREED** of people these days...

"Makes me **SICK!**"

Anyway, at least we're now able to buy **Powis** Road....

What're you giving for it?

"What're we **GETTING**, you mean?....Oh, not a **bad** price..."

We got twenty thousand off the asking price, for starters...and, after a bit of **argy-bargy**, the vendors said they'd throw in a **D Reg. Range Rover** and all the curtains...

"And they'd pay for our survey"

Well, that'll all be very nice...but what **we THOUGHT** we'd do, is to wait till the completion date... and then offer them **another six** grand less – **TAKE IT** or **LEAVE IT**...

"They'll buy **that?**"

"Oh yes! They're on their **KNEES** ...**desperate! Begging!**"

"Short and curlies department!"

Poor things!

© Posy Simmonds 1989

© Posy Simmonds 1989

A Christmas Carol

While Shepherd watched his stocks by night...
And monitored the pound...

...The other chaps went down the pub,
And Gloria stood a round.

Cheers, Gloria!

Cheery wearies!

God! Shepherd's a miserable sod!

Bloody SCROOGE!

Never stops, does he? Even at Christmas

Young Shepherd parked his Porsche that night
Close by his Dockland lair...
But cries of "Merry Christmas, Guv!"
Were wasted on the air...

Bah!

Humbug!

Happy Christmas!

As Shepherd sipped his Chambéry......
And wished the wine was colder,
The Ghost of Christmastide appeared
And tapped him on the shoulder....

Evening, Face-ache!

O God! Not ANOTHER break-in!

"Look here, old cock, this just won't do!
Now Total Candour speaks:
They say your meanness knows no bounds
—Your *rs***l* even squeaks.."

"Forget your bloody stocks and shares..!
Is Sentiment a sin?
'Tis Crimbotide, a time for thought
For neighbour, kith and kin."

Think of the Family...

My family?

Your mother dozing by the fire...
Your Dad hums 'Jingle Bells'.....

The cushions reek of old cigars
And foetid, sprouty smells....

Eeuch!

"Then spare a thought for those to whom
Dame Fortune deals hard knocks,
All ragged, lonely and unloved....
Their bed, a cardboard box...

"That some elect to find no work....
And end up tramps and junkies,
Then that's entirely their affair,
I couldn't give a monkey's!"

"And if you think I'll do a Scrooge,
And wish my fellow men
'A merry Christmas, one and all!'
Then you can think again!"

"Now, I must eat: my goose is cooked.
I'm sick of all your rhymes!"
...And at the microwave he sang
A carol for the times:

Have myself a Merry little Christmas...tra-la-la-la-la

Off went the Ghoul...and from the street
There came an eldritch squeat....

EEEEE!
E-E-E-E-EE!

...The Shade had tampered with some tyres
And widdled on a wheel....

A Merry Christmas One and All!